Three Kingdoms

Original Version by
Luo Guanzhong
Compiled and Illustrated by
Liu Zhenyuan

Morning Glory Publishers, Beijing

**Editors: Jiang Cheng'an
Du Juan**

Three Kingdoms
Original version by Luo Guanzhong
Compiled and illustrated by Liu Zhenyuan

Published by Morning Glory Publishers
35 Chegongzhuang Xilu, Beijing 100044,
China

Printed by Beijing Qianghua Printing House

Distributed by China International Book
Trading Corporation,
35 Chegongzhuang Xilu, Beijing 100044,
China
P.O. Box 399, Beijing, China
First Edition and First Printing

ISBN 7-5054-0492-X/J·0204

02800

88-E-499P

Printed in the People's Republic of China

Synopsis

The classic novel *Three Kingdoms* was attributed to Luo Guan-zhong in the 14th century. Because of the grand peasant up-rising in the end of the Yuan Dynasty, Luo came all the way to south of the Yangtze River, writing many works, such as *Romance of the Sui and Tang History*, *The Romance of the Five Dynasties*, *The Sorcerer's Revolt and Its Suppression by the Three Suis*, etc. He also wrote some plays, for example, *Meet by Emperor Tai Zu of the Song Dynasty*. The *Three Kingdoms*, however, was the most famous.

The novel *Three Kingdoms* depicts military compaigns and political intrigues between the kingdoms of Wei, Shu and Wu from A.D. 220 to 280; it is seven-tenths based on fact and three-tenths on imagination. Thereat the main characters and important events are all real people and historical facts, such as Cao Cao, Liu Bei, Sun Quan, Zhuge Liang, and the Yellow Scarves Uprising, Dong Zhuo's treacherous, the campaigns in Guandu and Chibi, etc. But many others are imaginary, for example's, the stories of Guan Yu's defeat in Maicheng, and his Green Dragon crescent-moon blade which actually did not weigh 82 *jin* (1 *jin*=0.5 kilogram), and also, the book exaggerated that Lü Bu's horse named Red Hare could "run a thousand *li* (1 *li*=0.5 kilometer) a day and wade through deep waters and climb over high mountains as easily as walking on a plain." All such things in the book are imaginary.

Therefore this is not a history book but a historical novel. This picture book, through more than 1,300 popular and easy-to-understand pictures, vividly illustrates the main characters and events described in the original works. A high artistic appreciation as well as some certain historic knowledge may be expected from the reading of it.

Liu Bei

Liu Shan

Zhuge Liang

Guan Ping

Zhou Cang

Guan Yu

Huang Zhong

Zhang Fei

Zhao Yun

Yan Yan

Jiang Wei

Ma Su

Ma Chao

Wang Yun

Diaochan

Lü Bu

Dong Zhuo

Cao Rui

Cao Ren

Cao Cao

Guo Jia

Xiahou Dun

Pang De

Yu Jin

Zhou Yu

Lu Su

Lu Xun

Sun Quan

Three Bold Spirits Swear Their Brotherhood in the Peach Garden

The Yellow Scarves Uprising broke out at Emperor Ling's time in the Eastern Han Dynasty.

Calls for volunteer soldiers had been delivered to Zhuo Prefecture.

Alas!

Why such long sighs?! A real man should be serving the emperor in the hour of peril.

My name is Zhang Fei; my styled name is Yide.

My name is Liu Bei; my styled name is Xuande.

Come! Let's have a few cups of drink.

Just then a well-built man was coming into the bar.

⑤

This man was Guan Yu, who styled himself Yunchang.

⑥

The three men drank together, talking very congenially.

⑦

For our mutual ambitions, I suggest we take an oath to be brothers from now on.

⑧

The three men went to a peach garden outside the village.

⑨

Liu Bei was the eldest, thus the first brother; Guan Yu the second and Zhang Fei the third.

Their followers numbered more than three hundred.

Three brothers went and followed Liu Yan, governor of Youzhou Prefecture.

The three brothers had many notable battles.

By the name of the Emperor, Liu Bei is appointed as a commander of Anxi County.

Several days later, the prefecture governor sent a government inspector to take office in Anxi County.

The county-level officials who don't fit their positions must all retire.

His Excellency doesn't feel well and refuses visitors.

My name is Liu Bei, and I've come to the service of His Excellency Governor Inspector.

20

He's come over with his hands empty. How can His Excellency receive him?

21

The Governor Inspector wields his power for money.

22

The three brothers visited the inspector together.

23

You've reported false merits and pretended royal relatives, so you should be removed from office.

24

5

Zhang Fei rushed in and dragged the inspector out of the office.

Forgive me, my good lord!

Let him off.

I won't keep this seal any more.

The three brothers went to Daizhou Prefecture to take refuge under Liu Hui.

Dong Zhuo Enters the Capital

Liu Bian was crowned after the death of the Emperor Ling.

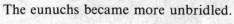

The eunuchs became more unbridled.

He Jin and Yuan Shao planned in secret to kill the eunuchs.

Any delay will cost the lives of all eunuchs.

The eunuchs took action ahead of He Jin and Yuan Shao, killing Commander General He Jin.

Kill all the eunuchs in the palace.

Eunuchs Zhang Rang and Duan Gui kidnapped the young emperor and King Chenliu, running away out of the palace gate.

Minister Lu Zhi cut off the two eunuchs' escape passage.

You damned eunuchs, let His Majesty be!

Zhang Rang and Duan Gui jumped into a river and killed themselves.

⑩

Lu Zhi escorted the emperor and his companions back to the capital.

⑪ ⑫

Soldiers reported that a troop appeared in the west.

I am Dong Zhuo, and I've come to ensure the security of the emperor.

His Majesty said outside armies aren't allowed to enter the capital.

⑬ ⑭

9

I've risked my life so that I can guard His Majesty, but you don't let me enter the capital. How can you do so?

Dong Zhuo entered the capital.

How can I control the ministers in the court and grasp power?

Just follow me. I'll treat you well.

One day Dong Zhuo led his troops past Yangcheng City.

Capture those people, kill the men and bring the women back to the capital.

Dong Zhuo must have won a battle.

Dong Zhuo is plotting an usurpation. Since he has so many troops, it's not so easy to eliminate him.

I want to dethrone the young emperor and enthrone King Chenliu as emperor.

11

Li Ru proposed that nobody else stood in the way except Ding Yuan.

Dong Zhuo was eager to kill Ding Yuan.

㉖ ㉗

Li Su told Dong Zhuo that Ding Yuan had an adopted son named Lü Bu who was peerlessly strong and brave.

Then you first draw Lü Bu over to our side.

㉘ ㉙

Dong Zhuo ordered to send Lü Bu some treasures and an excellent horse named Red Hare.

I, Lü Bu, would like to take Your Excellency as my adopted father.

㉚ ㉛

Lü Bu killed Ding Yuan in a plot.

Our this emperor is useless, so I want to dethrone him.

Lu Zhi protested.

Dong Zhuo wanted to kill Lu Zhi, but was prevented by Cai Zi.

None of the ministers dared to protest anymore.

Dong Zhuo thus crowned Emperor Xian and he took the office of Prime Minister.

13

Cao Cao resented Dong Zhuo.

I'd better escape from the capital before I get into trouble.

38

39

Cao Cao spent a night at Lü Boshe's home as he began to flee.

40

Why are they offering such hospitality? Is it a plot by Dong Zhuo?

41

This guy is rather hard to deal with, better tie him up before killing!

42

14

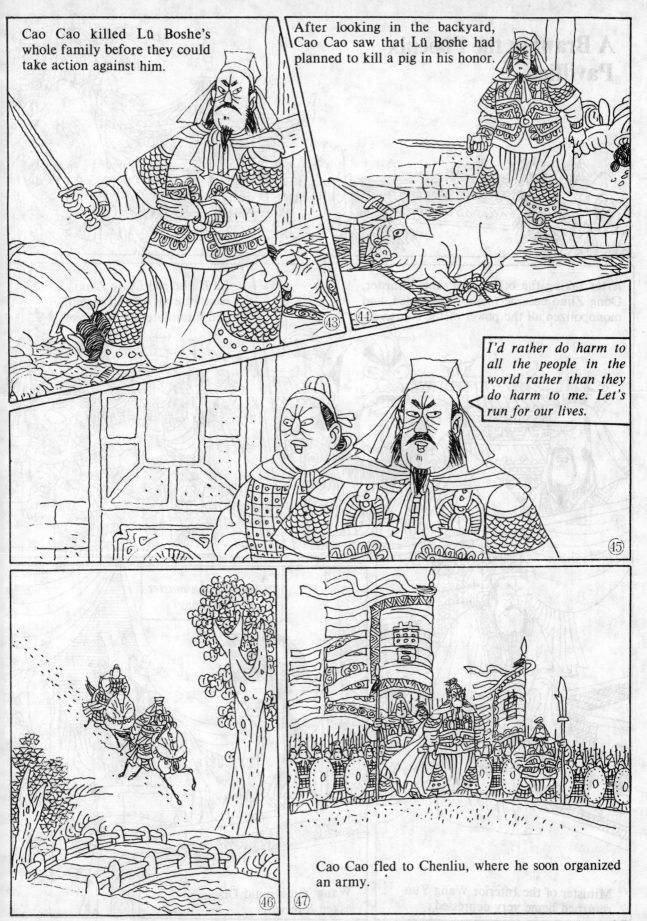

Cao Cao killed Lü Boshe's whole family before they could take action against him.

After looking in the backyard, Cao Cao saw that Lü Boshe had planned to kill a pig in his honor.

I'd rather do harm to all the people in the world rather than they do harm to me. Let's run for our lives.

Cao Cao fled to Chenliu, where he soon organized an army.

A Brawl in the Phoenix Pavillion

After taking the office of Prime Minister, Dong Zhuo became more unscruppled, and monopolized all the power of the court.

Lü Bu helped Dong Zhuo commit evils as well as bully and humiliate the ministers.

Why does the master feel so unhappy?

Minister of the Interior Wang Yun returned home very depressed.

Wang Yun's maid Diaochan asked him why.

18

How beautiful that leading dancer is!

She's my singing girl Diaochan.

Then Wang Yun presented Diaochan to Dong Zhuo.

I swear I'll save you.

Lü Bu, how dare you flirt with my beloved concubine!

Lü Bu has been flirting with me. Your Excellency must help me!

I swear to revenge Dong Zhuo for his wresting of my wife.

Lü Bu will do whatever Minister Wang arrange.

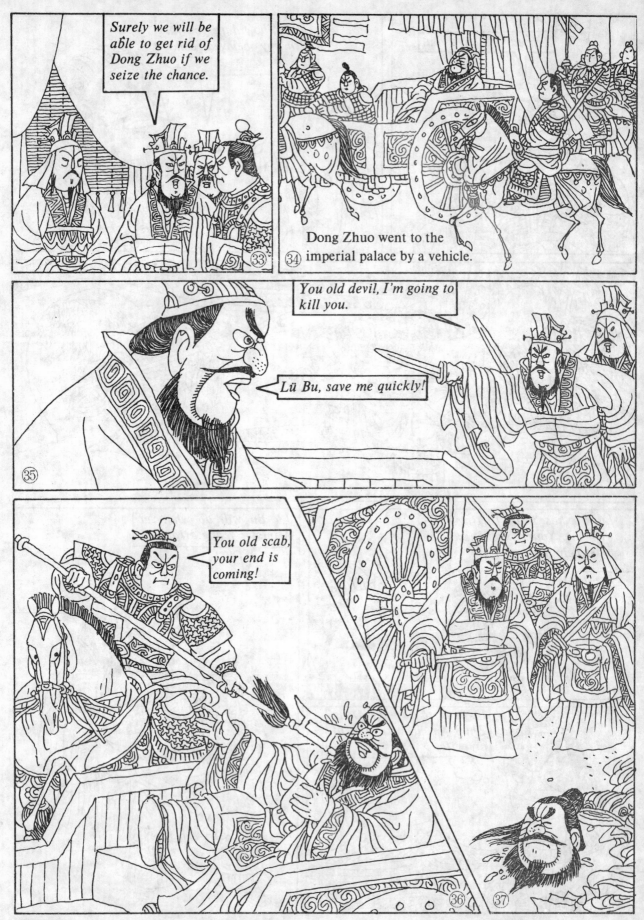

Reluctant to Rule Xuzhou

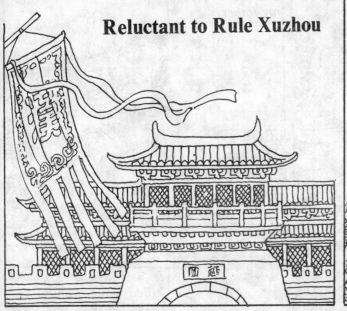

Cao Cao occupied Yanzhou by means of powerful forces.

Tao Qian, Governor of Xuzhou, ordered Zhang Kai to lead a group of soldiers to accompany the family.

Cao Cao sent men to Langya Prefecture so as to fetch his old father and other family members. Now they were on the way back.

Zhang Kai was planning to kill off the family in order to seize their property.

The family, together with the accompanying soldiers, took shelter from the rain half-way back. They were going to spent the night in the residence.

I shall sweep off Xuzhou to revenge my father.

Bad news governor, Cao Cao and his men are charging us.

It was Zhang Kai who killed your family and robbed their possessions. I wasn't with them.

Men, capture this old robber for me.

Tao Qian was driven back into Xuzhou City.

Tao Qian sent his men to Beihai Prefecture and asked Kong Rong for military help.

Kong Rong sent his own men to ask Liu Bei to move forces together with him.

We shall immediately attack Cao Cao's camps to rescue Xuzhou.

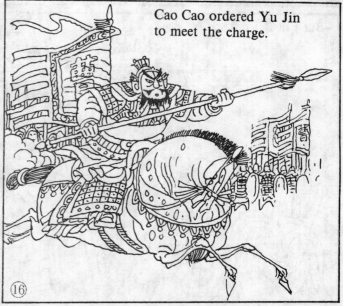

Cao Cao ordered Yu Jin to meet the charge.

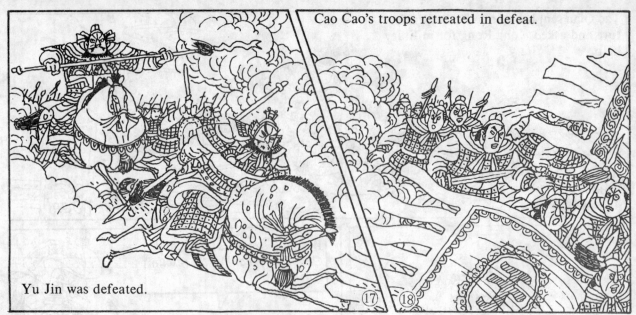

Yu Jin was defeated. ⑰

Cao Cao's troops retreated in defeat. ⑱

Liu Bei was entering Xuzhou with his troops. ⑲

I'm too old, so I'd rather give the authority of Xuzhou to you. ⑳

But Liu Bei refused. ㉑

Mi Zhu suggested, "This matter may be discussed after the troubles are over." ㉒

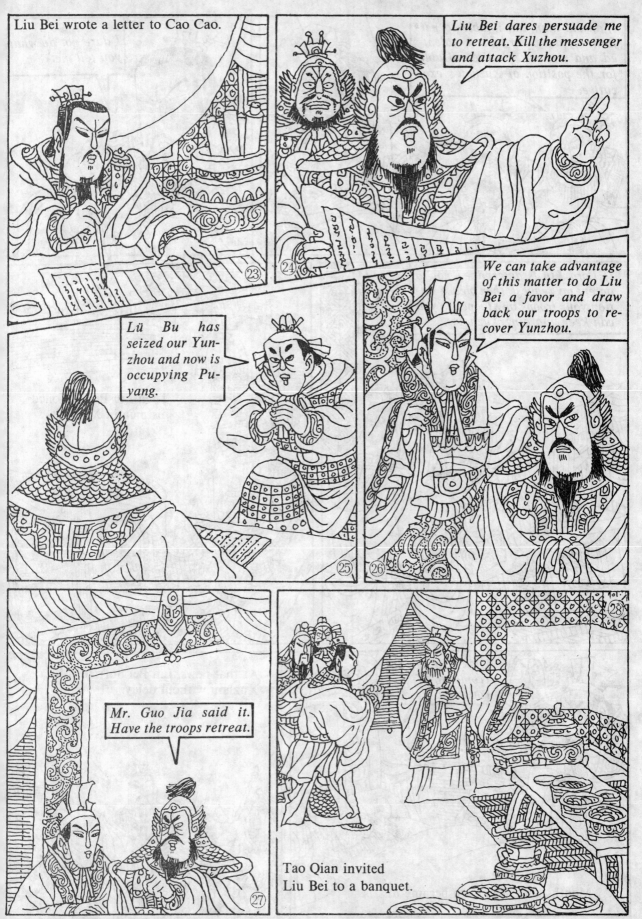

Liu Bei wrote a letter to Cao Cao.

Liu Bei dares persuade me to retreat. Kill the messenger and attack Xuzhou.

Lü Bu has seized our Yunzhou and now is occupying Puyang.

We can take advantage of this matter to do Liu Bei a favor and draw back our troops to recover Yunzhou.

Mr. Guo Jia said it. Have the troops retreat.

Tao Qian invited Liu Bei to a banquet.

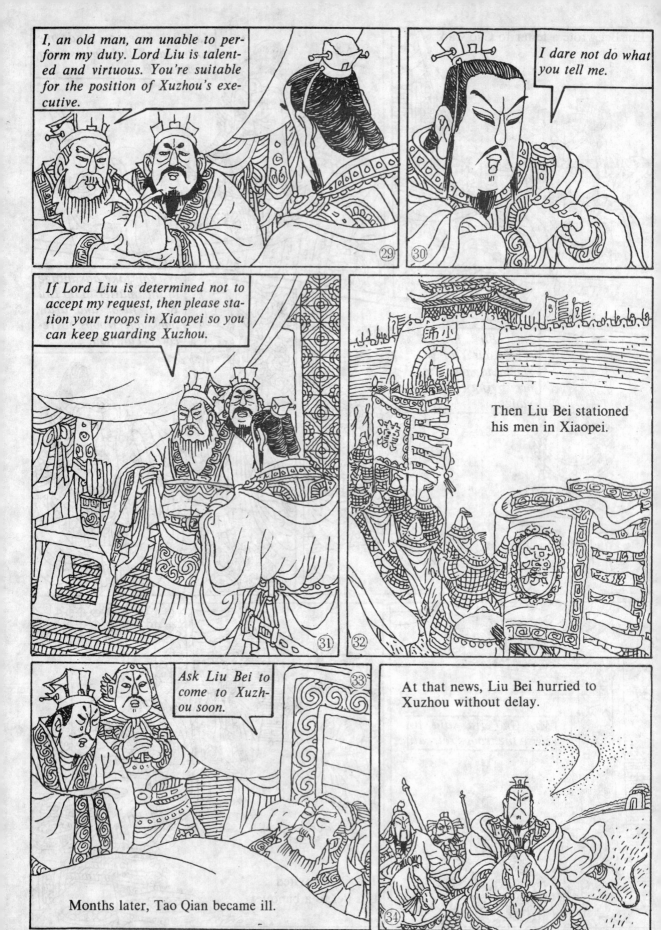

I, an old man, am unable to perform my duty. Lord Liu is talented and virtuous. You're suitable for the position of Xuzhou's executive.

I dare not do what you tell me.

If Lord Liu is determined not to accept my request, then please station your troops in Xiaopei so you can keep guarding Xuzhou.

Then Liu Bei stationed his men in Xiaopei.

Ask Liu Bei to come to Xuzhou soon.

At that news, Liu Bei hurried to Xuzhou without delay.

Months later, Tao Qian became ill.

I'm dying. I hope Lord Liu could treasure the territory for the Han Dynasty and accept the seal of Xuzhou's authority.

Tao Qian died of illness.

The officials argued that if Liu Bei didn't take the leading position of Xuzhou, the local citizens should suffer from turbulence.

Under this condition Liu Bei promised to temporarily take charge of Xuzhou.

As for the funeral, we are going to bury Tao Qian at the original place of the Yellow River.

Lü Bu Demonstrates His Marksmanship Before His Camp

Yuan Shu received the imperial seal during a time of turbulence. He had been planning to be emperor for a long time.

①

Yuan Shu wanted to send a punitive expedition under the name of the emperor against Sun Ce.

②

Yang Dajiang, however, advised him that he should suppress Liu Bei before assaulting Sun Ce.

③

General Ji Ling, you lead the forces to Xuzhou to attack Liu Bei.

④

⑤ *Rally with Lü Bu and make him assult Liu Bei from the other side.*

⑥ *Yuan Shu let me attack Liu Bei from the other side, and in return he promised to present me with money, grains and horses.*

⑦ Lü Bu commanded his forces against Liu Bei and occupied the latter's Xiapi City.

⑧ Under Yuan Shu and Lü Bu's attacks from both sides, Liu Bei escaped to Haixi.

⑨ *I have driven away Liu Bei, but Yuan Shu doesn't mention a word about the money, grains or horses.*

⑩ Chen Gong advised Lü Bu that Liu Bei could be invited back to station in Xiaopei so that he could fight in the vanguard when they attacked Yuan Shu in the future.

Liu Bei then stationed his forces in Xiaopei.

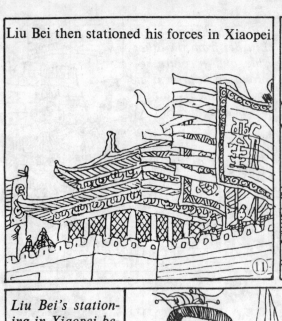

Yuan Shu sent Ji Ling to command his army in an assault against Liu Bei.

Liu Bei's stationing in Xiaopei benefits me. I should give him a hand.

Arrange our troops between the camps of Ji Ling and Liu Bei.

Lü Bu the busybody is putting his finger into our pie. Since his forces are between, how can we attack Liu Bei?

Invite Liu Bei and Ji Ling to my camp.

I, Liu Bei, am paying respect to General Lü.

I will help you through this crisis today. Please don't forget it in the future.

General Ji Ling is coming.

I'll not see him for a while.

I'm making peace for both of you. It will benefit both sides.
What is it you fear?

Are you going to kill me?

Liu Bei is my brother, so I plead that both sides yield.

Hit!

What should I say to my Lord Yuan Shu when I go back?

I've got an idea myself.

Take this letter to Yuan Shu.

Seeing Liu Bei enlarging his forces, Chen Gong advised Lü Bu to eliminate Liu Bei so as to avoid future danger.

Lü Bu commanded Zhang Liao, Gao Shun, Song Xian and Wei Xu to attack Liu Bei.

Our men are so few. We cannot match Lü Bu, so let's go to Cao Cao and ask for his refuge.

Liu Bei led his men as they forced their way out of the city.

Zhang Fei fought for the vanguard.

Guan Yu covered the retreat.

Liu Bei has gone to Cao Cao; he is now a long distance away from us.

Lü Bu Falls at White Gate Tower

Cao Cao commanded his forces to make war together with Liu Bei against Lü Bu.

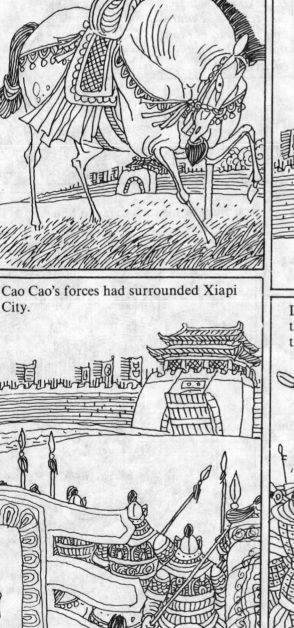

Lü Bu was defeated and fled to Xiapi.

Cao Cao's forces had surrounded Xiapi City.

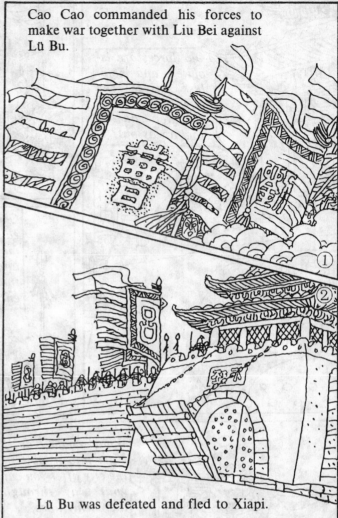

Lü Bu tried several times to break through the surrounding lines of troops, but failed.

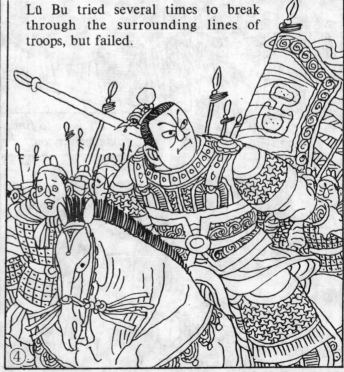

Our forces are isolated and helpless inside the city. However can we find a way out?

⑤

If you, General, will lead a group of excellent soldiers and station them outside the city, we can attack the enemy from both inner and outer sides. Then, Cao Cao will have to draw back his army.

⑥

Chen Gong's presented a good idea. Let me take a chance and try to break through the enemy's encirclement.

⑦

What should I do if I get into trouble in the city after you cut your way through the enemy lines?

⑧

Then I'll have to find another way out.

⑨

Lü Bu sent his men to Yuan Shu for help.

⑩

38

I can dispatch my troops for him, but I must take his daughter as my daughter-in-law.

So Lü Bu carried his daughter on his back and dashed out of the city.

Arrows flew in clouds from Cao Cao's camps.

Lü Bu had to return to the city.

Destroy the dike of the Yishui River and submerge Xiapi City.

39

I feel weak these days because of my indulgence in wine.

I, Hou Cheng, present some wine and meat for you, General.

Hou Cheng, I've ordered a prohibition on wine but you dare send me wine. Come, men, take him out and cut off his head.

The generals all knelt on the ground, asking Lü Bu's forgiveness for Hou Cheng.

Under Lü Bu's order, Hou Cheng was given 50 lashes with a stick.

40

Lü Bu indulges in wine and women and treats generals badly. We'd rather go to Cao Cao's refuge.

Hou Cheng stole Lü Bu's Red Hare and went to Cao Cao.

Song Xian and Wei Xu tied Lü Bu up when he was fast asleep and gave him over to Cao Cao.

Cao Cao's soldiers entered the city and Chen Gong was captured.

Zhang Liao, a senior general under Lü Bu was also captured by Cao Cao's soldiers.

Cao Cao you scab, now that I've been captured by you, the only thing I desire is death.

Execute Chen Gong, and send his mother, wives and children back to Xudu and provide care for them all of their lives.

Liu Bei, why don't you say a few favorable words for me?

How to deal with Lü Bu?

You, general, will make a decision yourself, please.

Take Lü Bu to the White Gate Tower and hang him.

Lü Bu was then hanged at the White Gate Tower.

I, Zhang Liao, only regret I couldn't kill you traitor in the battle.

I'll kill you first.

Such a loyal man should be spared and employed.

Cao Cao led his grand troops back to Xudu the capital.

Cao Cao himself untied Zhang Liao, and Zhang Liao surrendered to Cao Cao.

Cao Cao's Warming Wine and Rating the Heroes of the World

① Cao Cao and Liu Bei came to the court to pay their respects to Emperor Xian after they returned.

Emperor Xian addressed Liu Bei as Imperial Uncle for respect, and Cao Cao recommended Liu Bei to be a Left General.

②

③ Emperor Xian planned to go hunting.

④

The people that accompanied him thought it was the emperor who had shot a deer, therefore all shouted together: 'Long live to the Emperor!"

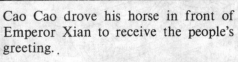
Cao Cao drove his horse in front of Emperor Xian to receive the people's greeting. .

Guan Yu was very angry at seeing Cao Cao oppressing the emperor.

Cao Cao usurps power and assumes control. He must plot against the imperial family in the future.

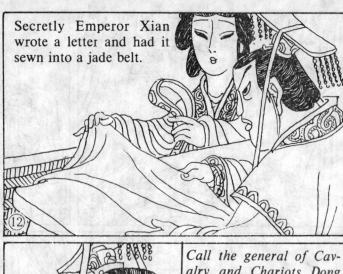

Secretly Emperor Xian wrote a letter and had it sewn into a jade belt.

Call the general of Cavalry and Chariots Dong Cheng in to see me.

I present you with a jade belt. You may examine it carefully at home.

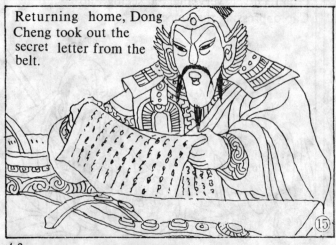

Returning home, Dong Cheng took out the secret letter from the belt.

Dong Cheng gathered his close followers to discuss a secret plan to eliminate Cao Cao.

We are at your service to help you brother to eliminate "the national scab."

We can ask the Imperial Uncle Liu Bei to help us.

Dong Cheng went to visit Liu Bei.

Cao Cao grabs power and he must rebel in future. I obey His Majesty to put him down and now I plead with Imperial Uncle to help.

Lord Dong suppresses the traitor under His Majesty's order, I will do my best to serve you.

Prime Minister Cao invites Imperial Uncle Liu over to his house for discussions.

I saw green plums in the trees, and coincidentally the wine has just been warmed, so I invite you here especially to have a chat.

Xuande, you've experienced a lot in your life, so you must be clear who the heroes of the world are. Please tell me.

I'm an ordinary man. How can I know a matter of that kind?

Xuande, please don't be so modest.

Really I'm ignorant about who are the heroes of this world.

Well, the living heroes of the world are just you and me!

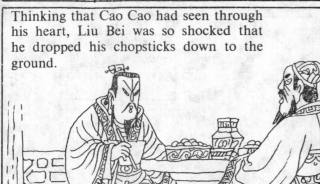

Thinking that Cao Cao had seen through his heart, Liu Bei was so shocked that he dropped his chopsticks down to the ground.

Coincidentally there occurred a thunder clap at that very moment. Cao Cao thought that Liu Bei was frightened by the thunder.

We heard our brother Liu was drinking with Mr. Prime Minister in here, so we came to offer our services.

Guan Yu and Zhang Fei dashed into the back garden.

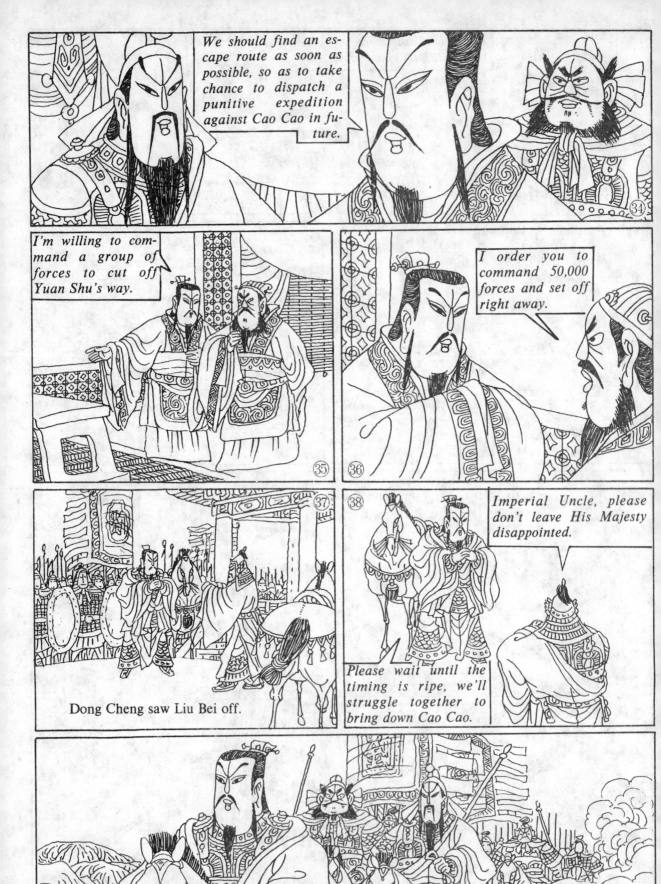

Dong Cheng and his fellows conspire to kill you, Mr. Prime Minister.

Seize all of Dong Cheng's family.

None of Dong Cheng's relatives have escaped, and this is an imperial letter written with blood that has been found.

Liu Bei has even signed his name to a list of people pledging to kill me.

Behead Dong Cheng, his other four fellows, and all members of the five men's families.

Guo Jia advised Cao Cao to get rid of Liu Bei so as to avoid future dangers for ever.

Dispatch troops to Xuzhou and capture Liu Bei alive for me.

Liu Bei and Zhang Fei were closely besieged.

Zhang Fei was protecting Liu Bei, fighting and fleeing.

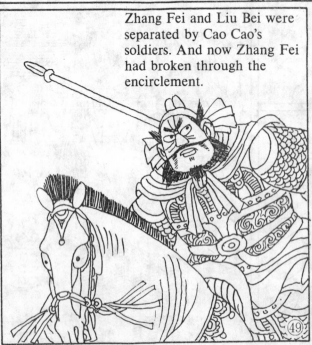

Zhang Fei and Liu Bei were separated by Cao Cao's soldiers. And now Zhang Fei had broken through the encirclement.

Liu Bei, without any companions following, ran for his life to the wild field.

Single Knight Guan Yu Returns to His Brother on a Thousand-li Horse

Guan Yu kept guard on Liu Bei's wives and child and fiercely defended the Xiapi City.

Cao Cao asked Xiahou Dun to curse and challenge Guan Yu below the city.

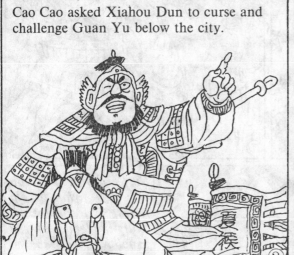

Guan Yu met the challenge.

Xiahou Dun was defeated and fled.

5 Guan Yu fell into a trap: Cao Cao's troops arrived when he was chasing the defeated challenger.

6 Guan Yu tried hard, but couldn't fight his way out.

7 A soldier reported that Xiapi City had been seized by Cao Cao's forces.

8 Cao Cao sent Zhang Liao to persuade Guan Yu to surrender.

9 *I'm grateful for you brother's favor in old times, so I come especially to plead with you to follow Lord Cao.*

10 *Now I've fallen in a trap. I'll just take death as calmly as going home. How can I surrender?*

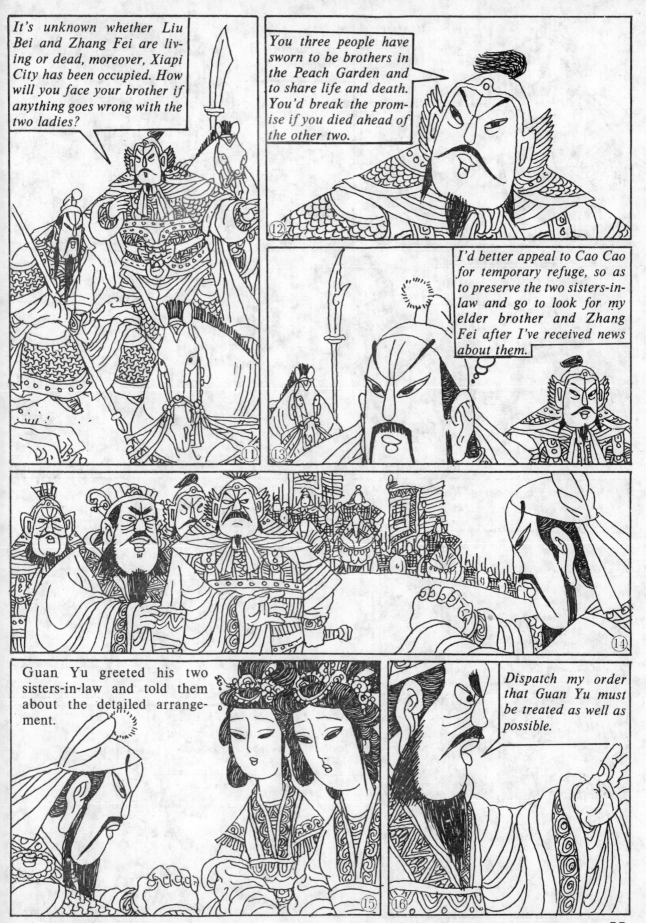

Prime Minister Cao had told his men to present some money and silk cloth.

Send them to my two sisters-in-law for storage.

Prime Minister Cao told us ten to serve you, general.

You all go to the inner yard and serve the two ladies.

This is Lü Bu's horse Red Hare, now I'd like to present it to you.

Thank you very much, Prime Minister!

This horse can run 1,000 li a day. With his help I can see my elder brother within one day once I know his whereabouts.

Yuan Shao dispatched Yan Liang to fight in the vanguard and the latter had subsequently killed Cao Cao's six senior generals in Baimapo.

I'll go and cut off Yan Liang's head to thank Prime Minister.

㉔

㉕

㉖

㉗

Cao Cao reported to the emperor to appoint Guan Yu as lord of Hanshou precinct.

㉘

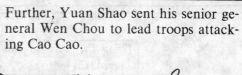

Further, Yuan Shao sent his senior general Wen Chou to lead troops attacking Cao Cao.

㉙

Cao Cao's senior generals Zhang Liao and Xu Huang were defeated subsequently.

Halt, Wen Chou!

After only a few rounds Wen Chou was beheaded and fell down his horse.

Cao Cao assigned Guan Yu to Runan to fight Yuan Shao's general Gong Du.

Gong Du, why do you betray the court?

You've betrayed your lord and now you are even scolding me!

Liu Bei is now under Yuun Shao's refuge. Why do you yield to Cao Cao?

Gong Du pretended to be defeated and fled.

I promise I'll take my two sisters-in-law to my elder brother!

Guan Yu returned to Xuchang, and Cao Cao came out of the city to meet him.

Guan Yu ordered his soldiers to prepare to leave Xuchang at night.

Guan Yu hung his seal, sealed the gold, and left in the night.

Guan Yu was hastily on his way at night.

Defense general Kong Xiu emerged in his way at the Dongling Pass.

From his mount, Guan Yu beheaded Kong Xiu.

Guan Yu killed Captain Meng Tan on the way to Luoyang.

Han Fu, the district governor of Luoyang, was also struck from his mount by Guan Yu.

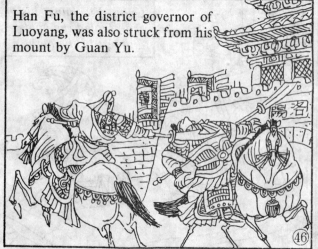

A soldier reported that the Yishui Pass was just ahead!

The Governor Liu Xi of the Yishui Pass was planning to murder Guan Yu.

Let Guan Yu settle in the Zhenguo Temple and hide sword-men there.

(48)

Ambush! Cautions!

(49)

(50)

Liu Xi was trying to flee, but one strike of Guan Yu's sword killed him.

(51)

(52)

When they arrived at Yingyang, the ruler Wang Zhi greeted Guan Yu and his followers at the official hotel.

Set a fire and burn them to death at mid-night.

(53)

Guan Yu and the others escaped from the fire and Guan Yu killed Wang Zhi.

At a passage port along the Yellow River General Qin Qi blocked their way.

Qin Qi also died by Guan Yu's sword.

Guan Yu ran into Zhang Fei in Gucheng.

Guan Yu, you have betrayed our elder brother and the principles of justice by submitting to Cao Cao. Now let's just fight to death.

The two ladies hurried to stop Zhang Fei.

Lord, Cao Cao has sent his top general Cai Yang to chase us.

Guan Yu finished off Cai Yang with just one blade strike.

Watch me kill Cai Yang to show my true feelings.

Zhang Fei jumped off his mount and paid his respects to Guan Yu.

Guan Yu and Sun Qian went to Yuan Shao and found Liu Bei. The three brothers met in Gucheng and were very excited.

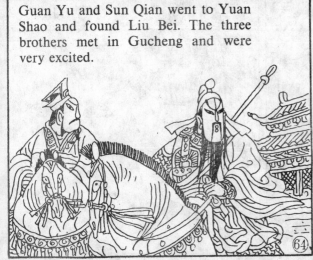

Liu Bei's Three Visits to Zhuge Liang

Liu Bei took refuge under Liu Biao of Jingzhou. He was hated by Liu Biao's step-wife Lady Cai because he dissuaded Liu Biao from passing over his elder son in favour of a younger son.

①

Lady Cai and Cai Mao conspired to murder Liu Bei.

②

Knowing that, Liu Bei fled in the night.

③

Yi Ji told of Lady Cai's plot to Liu Bei.

④

64

Soldiers reported that Liu Bei had run away.

⑤

⑥

Cai Mao led a group of troops after him.

Liu bei rode over the ten-metre-wide River Tan.

⑦

Liu Bei asked a little cowboy the way.

⑧

Are you Liu Xuande? I often hear my master, Still Water, talking about you.

⑨

Little brother, could you please bring me to Master Still Water?

⑩

65

⑪ Liu Bei paid his respects to Master Still Water.

⑫ If you are going to realize your ambitions, sir, you will surely win the country if you get the help of either the Sleeping Dragon or the Young Phoenix.

⑬ Liu Bei came across Xu Shu.

⑭ The Sleeping Dragon whom Master Still Water referred to is Zhuge Liang.

⑮ Zhuge Liang lives as a hermit in Sleeping Dragon Ridge, Longzhong. If you could get this man's help, it will be like the Han Dynasty winning Zhang Liang.

⑯

The three brothers set out together and arrived at Sleeping Dragon Ridge in Longzhong.

A lad said he didn't know where his master had gone.

Days later, the three brothers again went to Sleeping Dragon Ridge in the snow.

Master Zhuge is reading in the house.

I am the younger brother of Zhuge Liang and my name is Zhuge Jun. My brother has gone and is wandering around somewhere.

I'd like to leave a letter for Master Zhuge Liang. Please hand it to him. I will come to see him in the spring of next year.

In the spring of next year Liu Bei came once more to Longzhong.

This was the third time Liu Bei visited the Zhuges' hermitage.

The master is having a noon nap in the cottage.

We would like to wait outside.

Let me light the torch at the back of the house and see if that gets him up or not.

The lad wanted to waken the master, but was dissuaded by Liu Bei who said that would disturb the master.

㉙

Zhuge Liang woke up.

㉚

Imperial Uncle Liu has stood outside and waited for you for a long time.

㉛

Zhuge Liang hurried out of the inner house.

㉜

㉝

The two sat closely to each other talking about the nation's important events.

㉞

You, general, should take Jingzhou and make it your home base, then you can build your third of the triangle of power after Cao Cao and Sun Quan have built their.

㉟

You, master, can clearly shape national strategy without even walking a step out of your house. I plead to you master to lend me a hand.

㊱

I have been long content with my plow and mattock and hesitate to respond to the demands of the world. Forgive me if I am unable to comply with your demand.

㊲

Liu Bei was very sad at those words.

㊳

Zhuge Liang, seeing that Liu Bei was sincere, then agreed to go out of the hills with him.

㊴

㊵

Zhao Yun Rescues Master Liu Single-Handedly

Cao Cao personally led a powerful force to suppress Liu Bei.

①

Liu Bei was extremely worried about this news.

②

Jiangling is a very important spot in Jingzhou, it will be good if we can take Jiangling as a home base for the present.

③

That is just what I've planned.

④

Liu Bei sent Guan Yu to Jiangxia to ask Liu Qi for rescue troops.

⑤

Liu Bei arranged for Zhao Yun to protect members of his family and for Zhang Fei to cover the retreat. Then the troops set off to Jiangling.

⑥

We haven't received any message from Guan Yu. Dare I trouble you master go to Jiangxia for help in person?

⑦

Zhuge Liang set out to Jiangxia.

⑧

Liu Bei has only three thousand soldiers. But there are a hundred thousand civilians going with them. They moved forward covering just over ten li a day.

⑨

Go forward quickly, and catch up with Liu Bei within one day and night.

⑩

⑪

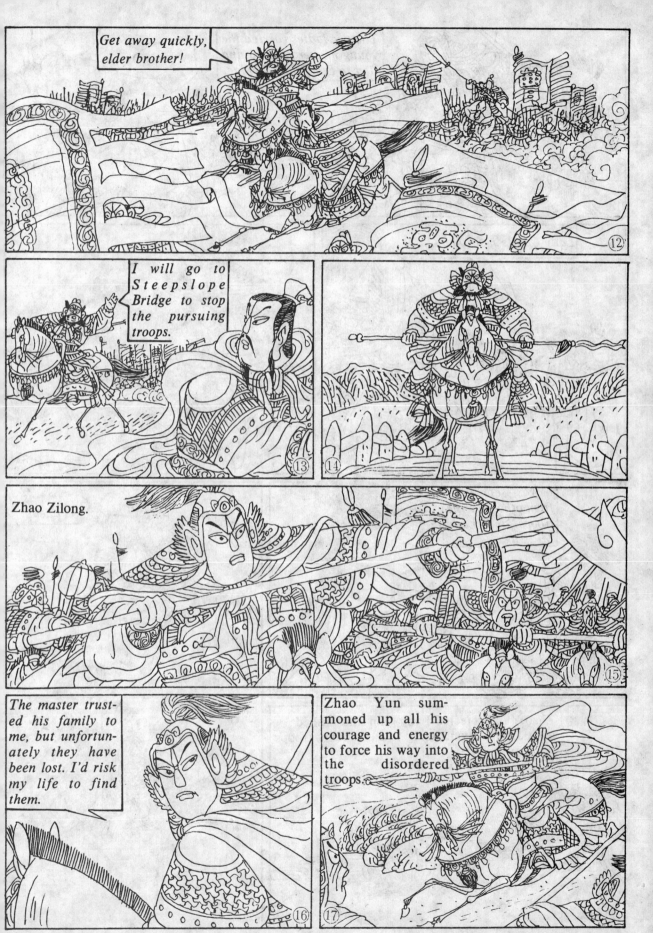

73

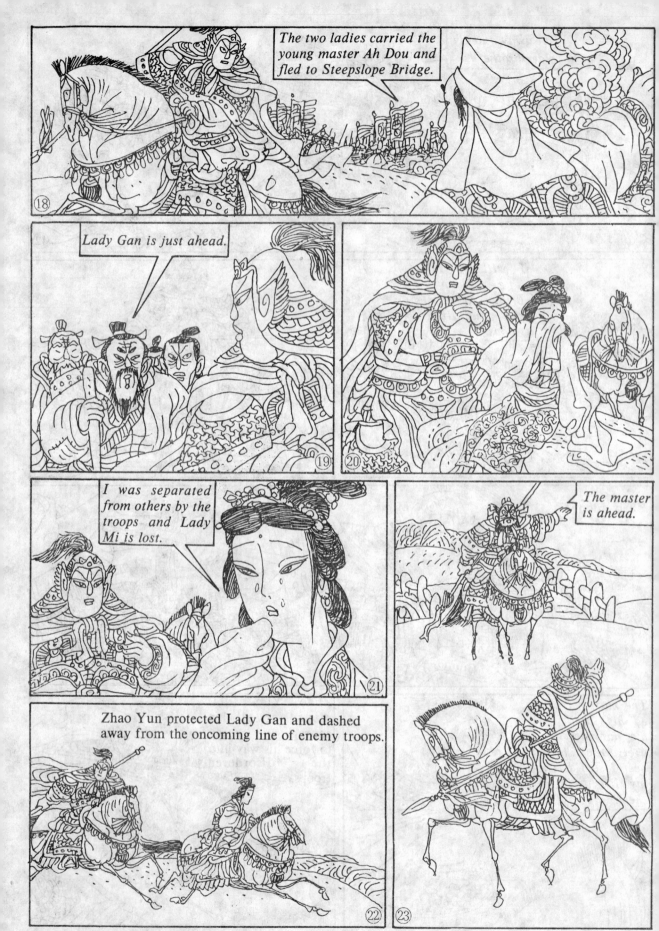

The two ladies carried the young master Ah Dou and fled to Steepslope Bridge.

Lady Gan is just ahead.

I was separated from others by the troops and Lady Mi is lost.

The master is ahead.

Zhao Yun protected Lady Gan and dashed away from the oncoming line of enemy troops.

I'll return to look for Lady Mi.

Zhao Yun stabbed Cao Cao's general, Xiahou En, to death.

From Xiahou En's hand Zhao Yun grabbed Cao Cao's precious sword Black Pommel.

Lady Mi is sitting there in a crevice in the wall.

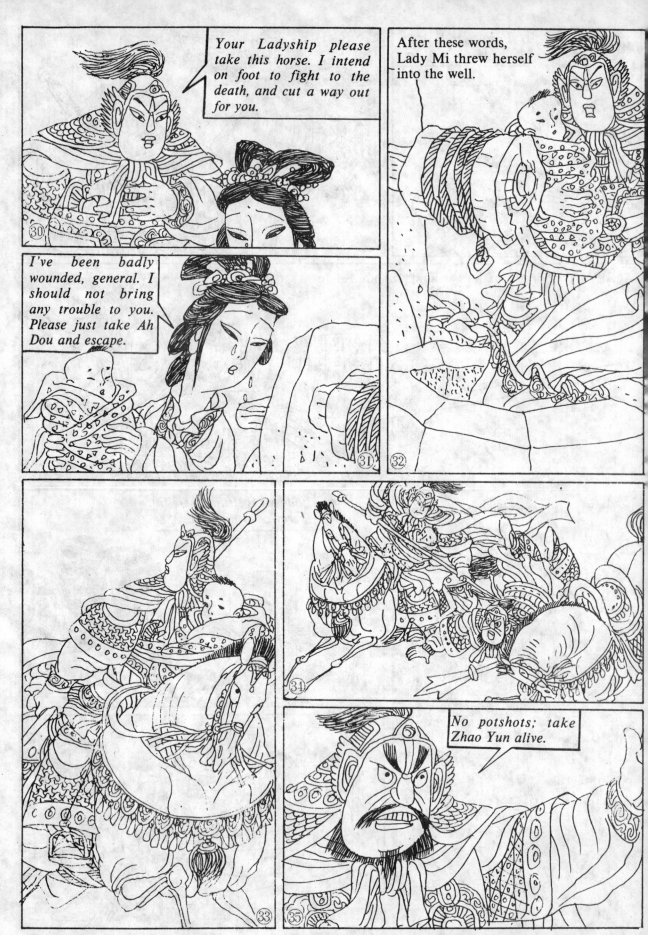

Zhao Yun killed Cao Cao's over fifty top generals.

Finally, Zhao Yun, bloody and exhausted, broke through the enemy's lines.

Quickly go your way, Zilong, and leave the pursuers to me!

Tie some branches on the horses' tails and drive them to raise the dust.

78

Draw back, quickly!

Pull down the bridge quickly.

For the sake of a suckling like him I risked losing a great commander!

Lady Mi was wounded and she threw herself down a well. By the favor of Heaven, the young master is safe.

Zhuge Liang Debates the Southern Officials

Cao Cao is too powerful. The best we can do is to turn to Sun Quan for support. If the south keeps Cao Cao at bay, keeping him northward, we can take advantage of the situation.

①

The Southland is well endowed with worthy men. Are they in need of us?

②

I'll go to the Southland to convince Sun Quan to resist Cao Cao with us.

③

Lu Su comes to offer Sun Quan's condolences for the death of Liu Biao.

④

Zhuge Liang was thinking of going to the Southland with Lu Su.

⑤

Zhuge Liang bade Liu Bei good-bye as he left for the Southland.

Lu Su invited Zhuge Liang to rest at the guesthouse while he went ahead to see Sun Quan.

Sun Quan was already in council with his officers and officials.

Cao Cao commands an army of one million. There is no opposing him. We would do better with the total security which submission would afford.

Zhang Zhao's views conform to the wishes of Heaven itself.

Lu Su suggested that Sun Quan make a master plan for the South as a much better way than submission.

But Cao's army seems impossible to resist.

⑫

I have brought Zhuge Liang back with me, and he will explain how things stand.

⑬

⑭

We heard that you have lost the Jingzhou Province to Cao Cao. How can you explain it?

⑮

We burned Cao out at Bowang, flooded him out at the White River, and the Cao army was in a state of panic and dismay. I am not sure that Guan Zhong and Yue Yi surpassed us in warfare.

⑯

83

To this oration Zhang Zhao had no reply. ⑰

Cao Cao has one million men. They glare down on us like tigers who could swallow Jiangxia, while your forces were ruined at Dangyang and Xiakou, what then? ⑱

How was Liu Xuande to hold off a million murderous men with a few thousand troops dedicated to humanity and honor? In the Southland the men are well trained and grain is plentiful. Yet you would have your lord submit to Cao. By your standards it's not Liu Xuande who fears Cao Cao! ⑲

Now the Han Dynasty's Heaven-ordained period draws to its close. All men tender Cao Cao allegiance while Liu Bei alone refuse to submit. He is bound to fail. ⑳

Cao Cao disavows his duty as a subject. Men of loyalty and filial devotion are pledged to help destroy him—for such is a true subject's obligation. You, Xue Jingwen, are a subject of the Han, how can you deny both king and father and render yourself unfit to speak in the company of men? ㉑

Both Yu Fan and Bu Zhi made no reply. ㉒

At this moment, Huang Gai entered the chambers.

Why not save your invaluable opinions for our lord!

These gentlemen's objections had to be answered.

Why hasn't Lord Liu submitted?

Liu Xuande is a hero, how could he be humiliated by submitting to Cao Cao the traitor!

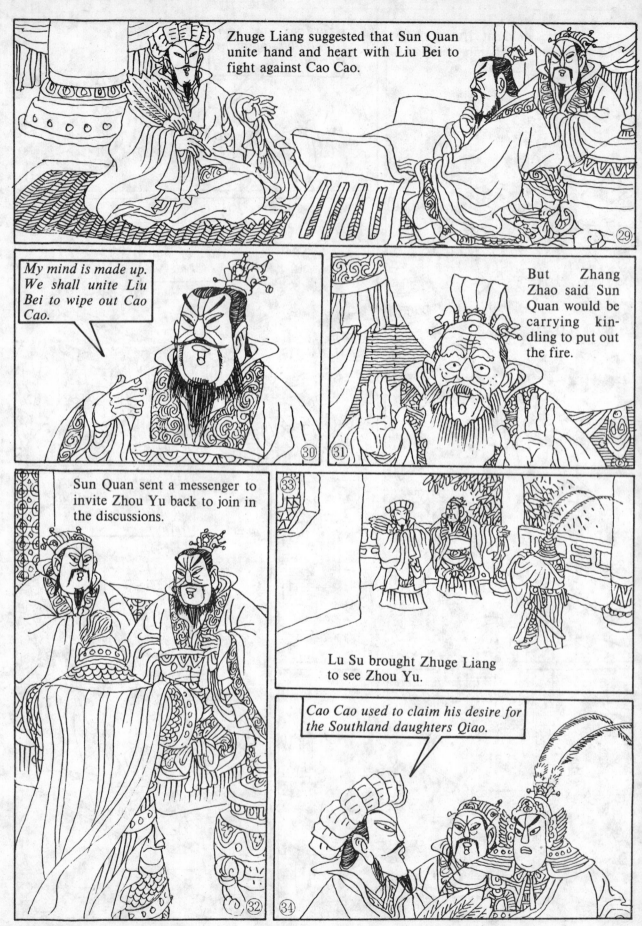

Zhuge Liang suggested that Sun Quan unite hand and heart with Liu Bei to fight against Cao Cao.

㉙

My mind is made up. We shall unite Liu Bei to wipe out Cao Cao.

㉚

But Zhang Zhao said Sun Quan would be carrying kindling to put out the fire.

㉛

Sun Quan sent a messenger to invite Zhou Yu back to join in the discussions.

㉜

㉝

Lu Su brought Zhuge Liang to see Zhou Yu.

Cao Cao used to claim his desire for the Southland daughters Qiao.

㉞

86

The elder daughter Qiao was the wife of Sun Ce, and the younger is my own wife. Cao Cao the traitor abuses us past endurance.

War or submission, I appeal to you to resolve it once and for all.

Your troops are keen and your grain stores ample. Now is the time for you to eliminate the enemy for the sake of the ruling house. How can we submit!

Grant me between fifty and a hundred thousand troops, and I will destroy the invaders for you.

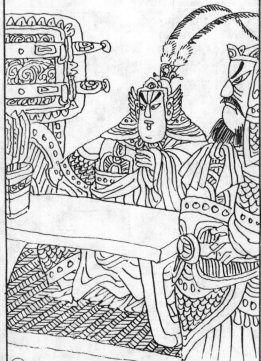

Zhou Yu gave orders to officers and officials to make preparation for war.

Any officer or official who advocates submission will be dealt with like this table!

The Battle at the Red Cliffs

Zhou Yu went to investigate Cao's naval encampment.

Cao's naval army is in neat and gallant array. Who's in general command?

Cai Mao and Zhang Yun.

Zhou Yu was cudgeling his brains thinking how to get Cai Mao and Zhang Yun out of the way.

At that moment, Jiang Gan from Cao's camp was announced to pay a call.

Zhou Yu was delighted by the news. He thought it a wonderful chance to get Cai Mao and Zhang Yun removed.

Jiang Gan slipped out of the tent before dawn and hurried back to Cao's camp.

⑫

Cai Mao and Zhang Yun want to kill you and then submit to Zhou Yu.

⑬

Please convey my felicitations to the chief commander.

Cao Cao believed Jiang Gan and had Cai Mao and Zhang Yun executed.

⑭ ⑮

Seeing that Zhuge Liang had seen through the trick, Zhou Yu felt jealous and decided to kill him to cut off the roots of future trouble.

⑯

⑰

One day Zhou Yu asked Lu Su to invite Zhuge Liang to the assembly.

90

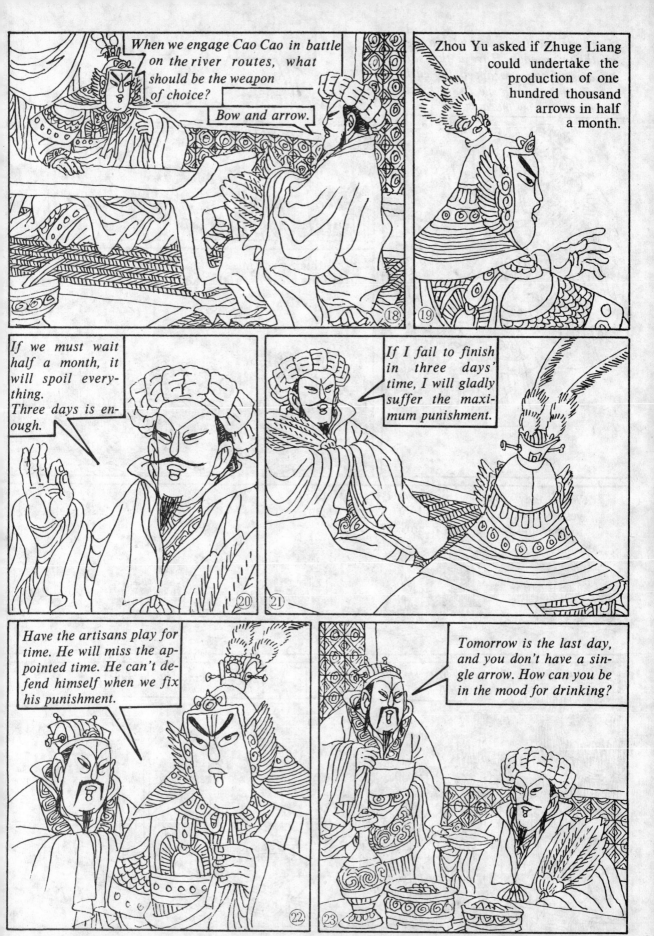

Lend me twenty vessels, with a crew of thirty on each. Have a thousand bundles of straw wrapped for each vessel, and go with me to fetch the arrows tomorrow morning.

From where?

You'll see.

With thick river mists Zhuge Liang urged his boats on to the north.

When they were nearing Cao's river base the vessels advanced in single file. The crews began to roar and pound their drums.

What if they make a sally?

They dare not in the fog.

Cao Cao ordered archers and cross-bowmen to shoot at the enemy.

When the sun climbed, dispersing the fog, Zhuge Liang ordered the boats to hurry homeward.

Zhou Yu came out of his tent to greet Zhuge Liang.

The arrows in twenty boats totaled over one hundred thousand.

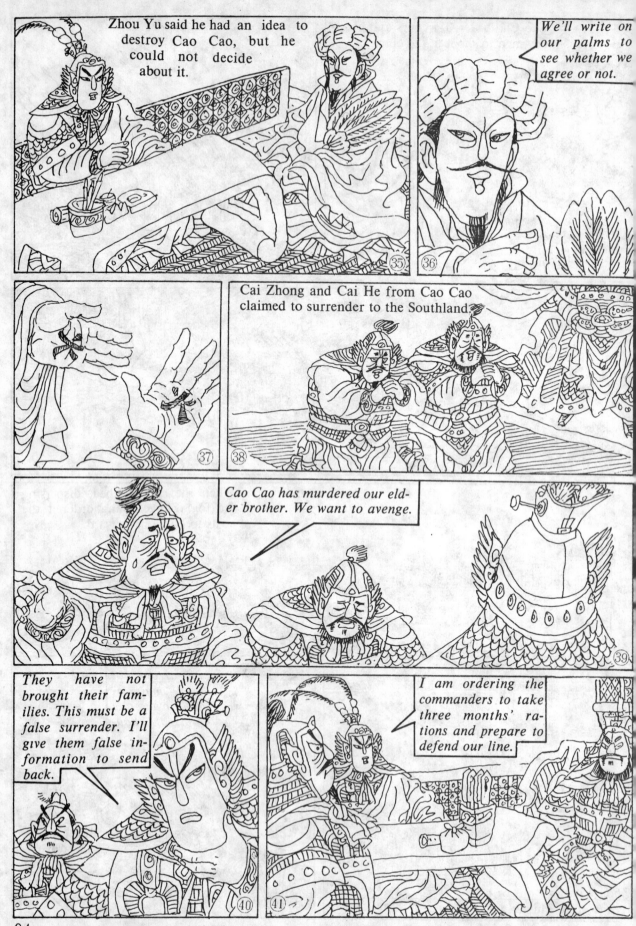

94

48

Huang Gai asked Kan Ze to deliver a letter of surrender to Cao Cao.

Huang Gai was brutally and gratuitously beaten today. He wants to defect and asks me to present his secret letter.

49

You dare carry a letter of sham surrender here. Remove and execute him.

50

It seems like a real surrender.

52

Cai Zhong and Cai He send back a secret letter.

51

Cao Cao asked Kan Ze to return south to complete the arrangements with Huang Gai for the date.

53

54

Jiang Gan brought Pang Tong to Cao Cao's presence.

Your great name has long been familiar to me, may I expect your advice and instructions?

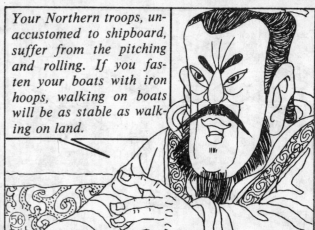

Your Northern troops, unaccustomed to shipboard, suffer from the pitching and rolling. If you fasten your boats with iron hoops, walking on boats will be as stable as walking on land.

Have blacksmiths in the army to manufacture hoops and bind the boats.

Your Excellency, though the linked ships are level and stable, if the enemy attacks with fire it will be hard to escape.

Now at winter's depth, how could there be a south wind or east wind? If they use fire, they will only burn out their own troops.

Sir, the chief commander has fallen with blood foaming up in his mouth. He has lost consciousness.

I have a prescription which can cure you.

To break Cao's back, with fire we attack. Everything is set, save the east wind we lack!

I can work certain charms on the platform to borrow southeast wind for you.

Zhou Yu's three routes of troops attacked from the west and east of the Red Cliffs.

Zhang Liao helped Cao Cao out of the fire.

Guan Yu, obligated by Cao Cao, released him at Huarong Trail. Cao Cao and his remnants fled back to Xuchang.

Fight at Changsha

When Sun Quan and Cao Cao's troops were fighting for territory, Zhuge Liang effortlessly captured Nanjun, Xiangyang and Jingzhou.

Afterwards he occupied Lingling, Wuling and Guiyang.

Zhang Fei and Zhao Yun has each taken a district, why don't I ask to be given the task of taking Changsha.

We can let Zhang Fei defend Jingzhou and Guan Yu attack Changsha.

⑤

You'll need extra troops, for Han Xuan, the governor of Changsha, has a general, Huang Zhong, who is invincibly courageous.

With my own company of five hundred expert swordsmen, I guarantee that the head of Huang Zhong will be presented for you.

⑥

Guan Yu set out for Changsha with his troops.

⑦

Guan Yu comes for Changsha. What shall we do?

⑧

The great general Huang Zhong need not fight. I, Yang Ling, will capture him alive.

⑨

Guan Yu waved his sword and came for Yang Ling.

⑩

Ah!

⑪

Guan Yu chopped Yang Ling down. Seeing this, Huang Zhong, sword in hand, raced out of the city.

⑫

The two began to fight.

⑬

They struggled through several passes without a victor.

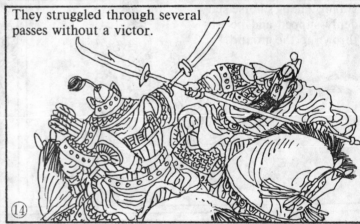

⑭

Han Xuan rang the gong calling Huang Zhong and his men back.

⑮

Guan Yu, seeing Huang Zhong deserved his reputation, planned to use the "trailing sword trick" in the next day's fight.

⑯

The next day Huang Zhong came out fighting Guan Yu again.

⑰

Guan Yu wheeled and fled, preparing for the "trailing sword trick."

⑱

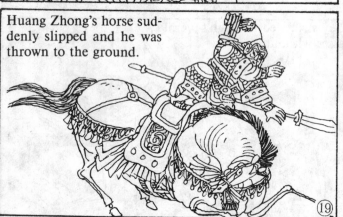

Huang Zhong's horse suddenly slipped and he was thrown to the ground.

⑲

Come on! I spare you. Get another horse and let's finish this.

⑳

Why don't you shoot?

㉑

He didn't kill me. How can I shoot him!

㉒

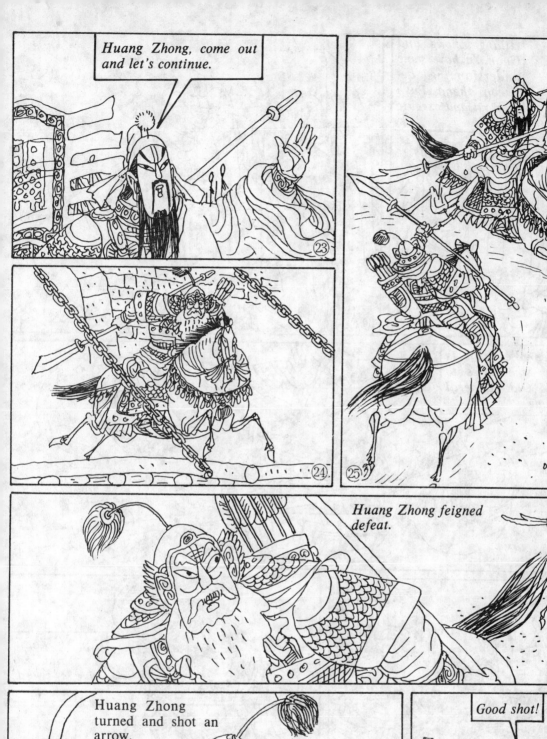

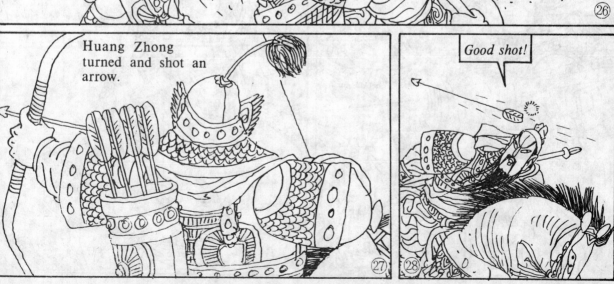

Wei Yan killed Han Xuan and offered the city to Guan Yu.

Huang Zhong stays at home, unwilling to submit.

Liu Bei and Guan Yu went to Huang Zhong's home to extend the invitation to submit.

You are so kind to me. I submit.

Liu Bei and his enormous troops returned to Jingzhou in triumph.

The Sweet Dew Temple

① Liu Bei had borrowed Jingzhou from Zhou Yu as his temporary base and had no intention to restore it to the Southland. Zhou Yu felt indignant about it.

② Lu Su said Zhuge Liang planned to restore Jingzhou after they settled the western province of the Riverlands.

③ Liu Bei's wife, Lady Gan died. They are arranging the funeral now.

④ I have a plan that will get Jingzhou with no effort at all.

⑤ Liu Bei's wife is dead. I'll propose to our lord that he send a go-between to Jingzhou and convince Liu Bei to marry our lord's sister. We'll put him under house arrest when he comes, and demand Jingzhou in exchange for his release.

Sun Quan sent Lu Fan to Jing-zhou as the go-between.

Lu Fan said Sun Quan would like to marry his own sister to Liu Bei.

This is Zhou Yu's trick. But I have a little "plan" to make sure you make Sun Quan's sister your wife without losing Jing-zhou.

Zhou Yu plans to murder me. How can I walk lightly into this trap?

Follow my plan and there is not the slightest risk.

Zhuge Liang called Zhao Yun and whispered a few confidential words to him.

Liu Bei, together with Sun Qian and Zhao Yun, and some followers, set out for Nanxu.

109

At Zhao Yun's order the followers bought bands of red silk to drape over their shoulders, and spread the news of the marriage among the folk people.

⑫

Liu Bei went to pay his respect to State Elder Qiao.

⑬

State Elder Qiao, after receiving Liu Bei, went at once to offer his congratulations to the State Mother, Lady Wu.

⑭

Quickly call Sun Quan here to see me.

⑮

The State Mother questioned Sun Quan why he didn't tell her anything about the marriage.

⑯

Who told you that, mother?

⑰

The whole city knows.

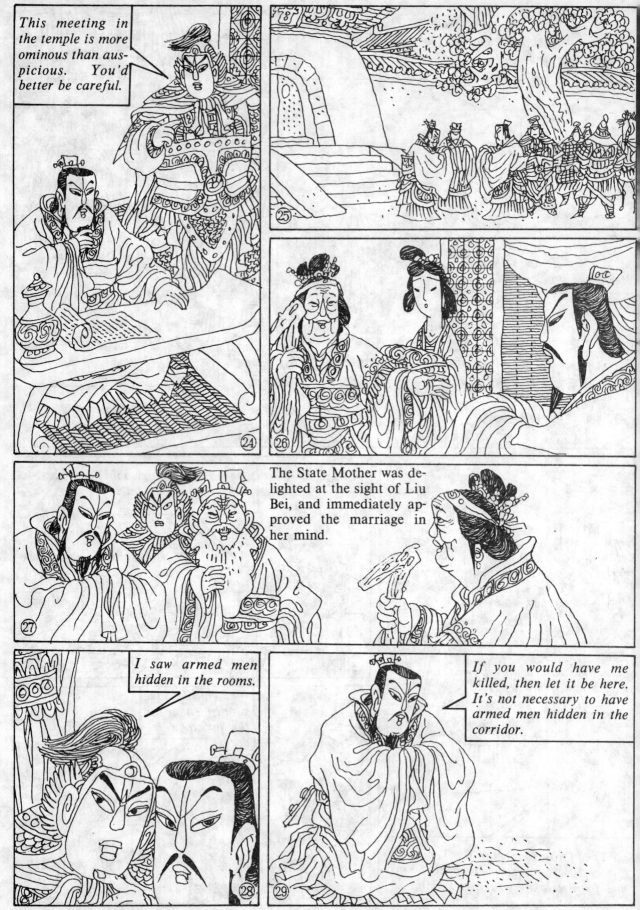

This meeting in the temple is more ominous than auspicious. You'd better be careful.

The State Mother was delighted at the sight of Liu Bei, and immediately approved the marriage in her mind.

I saw armed men hidden in the rooms.

If you would have me killed, then let it be here. It's not necessary to have armed men hidden in the corridor.

112

Today Liu Bei has become my son-in-law. Who dare to hurt him!

Why are you still here? Get out!

Get away quickly!

You move to my residence and we'll choose an auspicious day for the wedding.

Sun Quan hurriedly sent a messenger to Zhou Yu with the news.

Seeing that the ruse had been turned into reality, Zhou Yu was shocked.

Capture of Chengdu

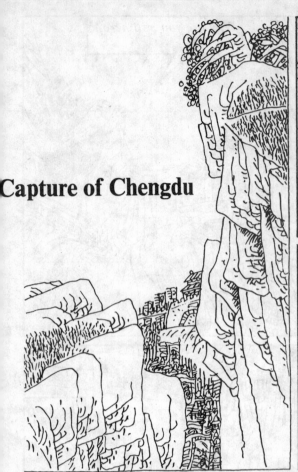

Zhuge Liang dispatched troops to the west province of the Riverlands. He ordered Zhang Fei to attack Bajun.

①

Zhao Yun was dispatched to meet Zhang Fei at Luocheng.

②

Zhang Fei arrived at Bajun, bellowing to challenge Yan Yan to a fight every day.

③

Since no one came out to meet Zhang Fei, he thought of a way to induce them out.

Yan Yan, the governor of Bajun, refused battle.

④

⑤

115

You are so generous. I will submit.

(12)

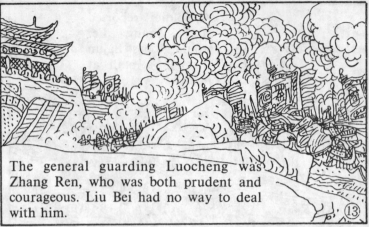

The general guarding Luocheng was Zhang Ren, who was both prudent and courageous. Liu Bei had no way to deal with him.

(13)

Zhang Ren came out of the city to challenge Liu Bei to battle.

(14)

Zhang Fei met him. After several passes Zhang Ren feigned defeat.

(15)

Zhang Fei came after him and was trapped.

(16)

(17)

Zhao Yun and his troops came in time and saved Zhang Fei.

Tomorrow at the Gold Goose Bridge, we'll capture Zhang Ren.

⑱

⑲

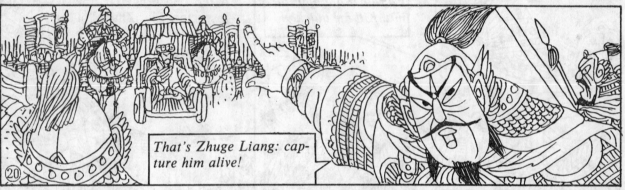

That's Zhuge Liang: capture him alive!

⑳

㉑

We are trapped!

㉒

Zhang Ren, I've been waiting for you a long time!

㉓

Zhang Ren fled to the hills and was captured alive.

I'd rather die than submit. Kill me quickly!

Execute him to preserve his reputation for loyalty.

After Luocheng fell, the Inspector Liu Zhang of Yizhou went to seek help from Zhang Lu.

Zhang Lu ordered Ma Chao to attack Jiameng Pass.

Liu Bei and Zhang Fei went to its rescue. ㉚

㉛

Light the torch-es and we'll fight!

㉜

㉝

Ma Chao was bold and brave.

㉞

㉟

Zhuge Liang planned to induce Ma Chao to surrender.

Zhuge Liang sent Sun Qian to convince Zhang Lu to change his mind.

If you do not give help to Liu Zhang, when it's all over I will recommend you as king of Hanning.

Zhang Lu does not trust me. I can neither help Liu Zhang nor go to see Zhang Lu. What shall I do?

Zhang Lu sent orders for Ma Chao to cease fighting.

Imperial Uncle Liu is courteous to the worthy and humble before men of ability. Why not turn from the benighted Zhang Lu and make your future with the enlightened Xuande?

Ma Chao submitted to Liu Bei.

Liu Zhang, I've submitted to Imperial Uncle Liu. Quickly surrender and present Chengdu.

43

Xu Jing, the district governor of Shu, has also submitted to Liu Bei. Chengdu is now difficult to hold.

44

I have decided to surrender so that the people of Chengdu do not have to suffer war.

45

When Liu Bei occupied Chengdu, he proclaimed himself inspector of Yizhou.

46

Liu Bei bestowed on Liu Zhang the insignia of General Who Exhibits Might and had him move to Jingzhou.

With the Riverlands as his base, Liu Bei had achieved a triangular balance of power with Cao Cao and Sun Quan.

47

48

Guan Yu Floods Cao Cao's Seven Armies

After occupying the Riverlands, Liu Bei defeated Cao Cao at Hanzhong and enthroned himself as the King of Hanzhong.

Unable to have Liu Bei return Jingzhou, Sun Quan decided to coordinate with Cao Cao to attack Liu Bei.

This is not at all unexpected. We can have Guan Yu capture Fan. That should make the enemy scatter.

Pan Rui guard Jing-zhou and I'll go to attack Fan.

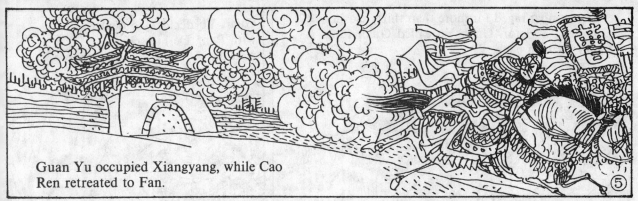

Guan Yu occupied Xiangyang, while Cao Ren retreated to Fan.

Guan Yu moved his army directly to Fan.

Cao Cao sent Yu Jin and Pang De with their forces to relieve Cao Ren's siege at Fan.

Pang De brought a coffin with him, intending to fight Guan Yu to the finish.

Pang De is bellowing outside our tent.

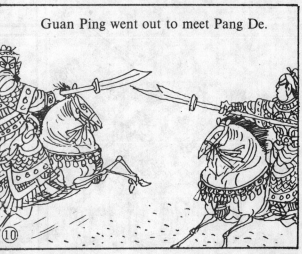

Guan Ping went out to meet Pang De.

The combat raged for more than thirty clashes without a victor. Guan Yu called Guan Ping and his men back.

Guan Yu decided to deal with Pang De himself the next day.

Guan Yu returned to his camp.

Yu Jin and Pang De have stationed their seven armies at the mountain passes north of Fan.

Guan Yu brought Guan Ping with him to watch the landform.

Yu Jin and Pang De have deployed their troops in a ten-li valley. They are doomed.

Guan Yu gave orders to have all drainage points dammed.

It was autumn. Heavy rainstorms kept on striking. The Xiang River overflowed.

125

During a night of fierce wind and heavy rain, Guan Yu ordered his men to release the water.

The seven armies were all drowned by the flood.

Climb up the hill for shelter.

Yu Jin, Pang De, submit quickly.

Yu Jin surrendered to Guan Yu.

Pang De, grabbing a boat, tried to flee away.

Zhou Cang rode a raft to hit Pang De's boat, overturned it and caught Pang De alive.

Guan Yu beheaded Pang De.

Guan Yu led his force to attack the city of Fan.

Cao Ren ordered his bowmen to shoot.

The arm is greenish and swollen. The arrowhead must have been poisoned.

Guan Ping sent people to search high and low for a good doctor.

Master Hua Tuo came to cure Guan Yu.

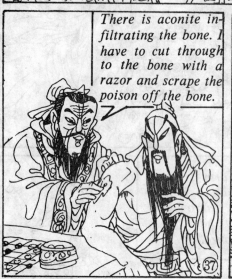

There is aconite infiltrating the bone. I have to cut through to the bone with a razor and scrape the poison off the bone.

It is Your Lordship who is more than human.

The arm is as flexible as ever. Master, you are a marvelous physician!

Guan Yu Flees to Mai in Defeat

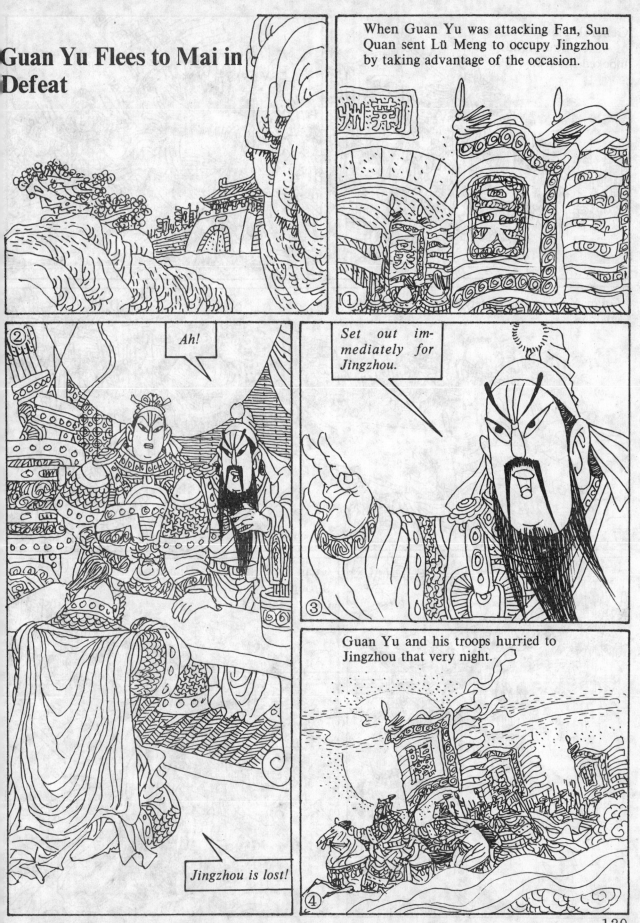

When Guan Yu was attacking Fan, Sun Quan sent Lü Meng to occupy Jingzhou by taking advantage of the occasion.

①

② Ah!

Set out immediately for Jingzhou.

③

Guan Yu and his troops hurried to Jingzhou that very night.

④

Jingzhou is lost!

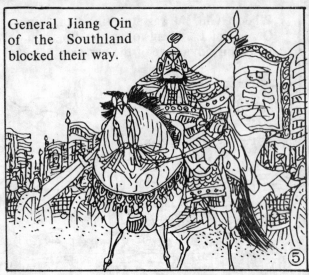
General Jiang Qin of the Southland blocked their way.

Guan Yu was completeiy surrounded by the enemies.

Guan Ping and Liao Hua broke through the encirclement and rescued Guan Yu.

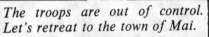

The troops are out of control. Let's retreat to the town of Mai.

Guan Yu arrived at Mai with his remnant.

The Southland troops came after them and surrounded Mai.

Liao Hua broke out and went to Shangyong for help.

Our army is not strong enough for the rescue.

Liao Hua then headed for Chengdu which was a thousand *li* away.

Sun Quan sent Zhuge Jin to talk Guan Yu into submission.

(16)

How can a real man surrender! Drive him away!

(17)

(18)

The grain is exhausted and no help comes. What shall we do?

Zhao Lei suggested that Guan Yu abandon Mai and flee for the Riverlands, and plan the reconquest of Jingzhou later.

(19)

(20)

(21)

Guan Yu was captured and taken to Sun Quan, who asked him if he acknowledged himself beaten.

I gave my allegiance to Imperial Uncle Liu in the peach garden when we swore to uphold the house of Han. Now death alone remains. There is no more to say.

I propose that we encourage him to come over to us. What do you say?

So I should kill him.

It will not work. Guan Yu is so loyal and courageous that years ago Cao Cao failed to hold him with many kindnesses. If you do not do away with him today, I fear the consequences.

Sun Quan admitted the truth and finally beheaded Guan Yu and his son.

This great hero has died early!

Lu Xun Burns Liu Bei's Camps

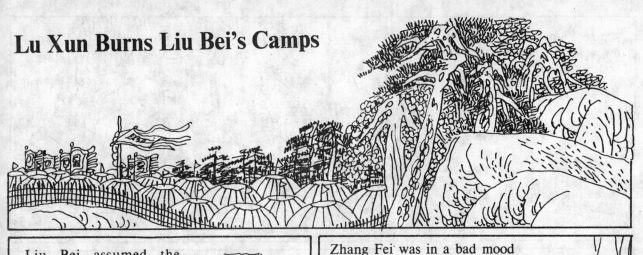

Liu Bei assumed the throne in Chengdu and named the dynasty as Shu. ①

Zhang Fei was in a bad mood because of Guan Yu's death. He often flogged his men to vent his grief. ②

③

Two minor commanders, Fan Jiang and Zhang Da killed Zhang Fei while he was sleeping, and fled for the Southland.

Guan Yu, Zhang Fei and I pledged our honor to live and die for each other. I swear not to live if I can not avenge them!

④

Set out for the Southland immediately!

⑤

Zhuge Liang stayed to guard Chengdu, while Liu Bei was heading for the Southland with his enormous number of troops.

Sun Quan sent Lu Xun to confront Liu Bei.

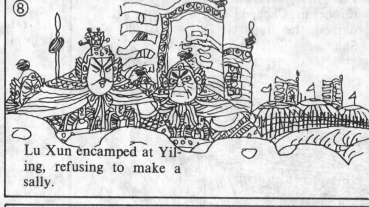

Lu Xun encamped at Yiling, refusing to make a sally.

Liu Bei and his force arrived at Yiling.

Liu Bei had his warrior challenge for a fight every day.

Lu Xun did not respond.

Soon it was summer and the weather became scorching hot.

⑫

Liu Bei moved his army into the woods where the shade afforded some relief from summer's heat.

⑬

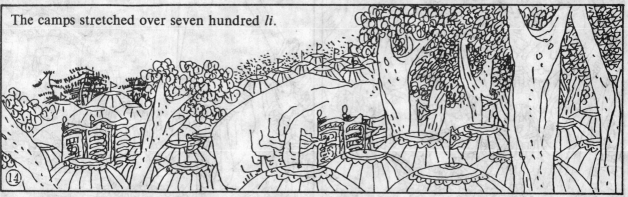

The camps stretched over seven hundred *li*.

⑭

We'll defeat the Riverlands army in a few days.

⑮

Tonight when the southeast wind blow, set fire to the Riverlands camps.

⑯

⑰

137

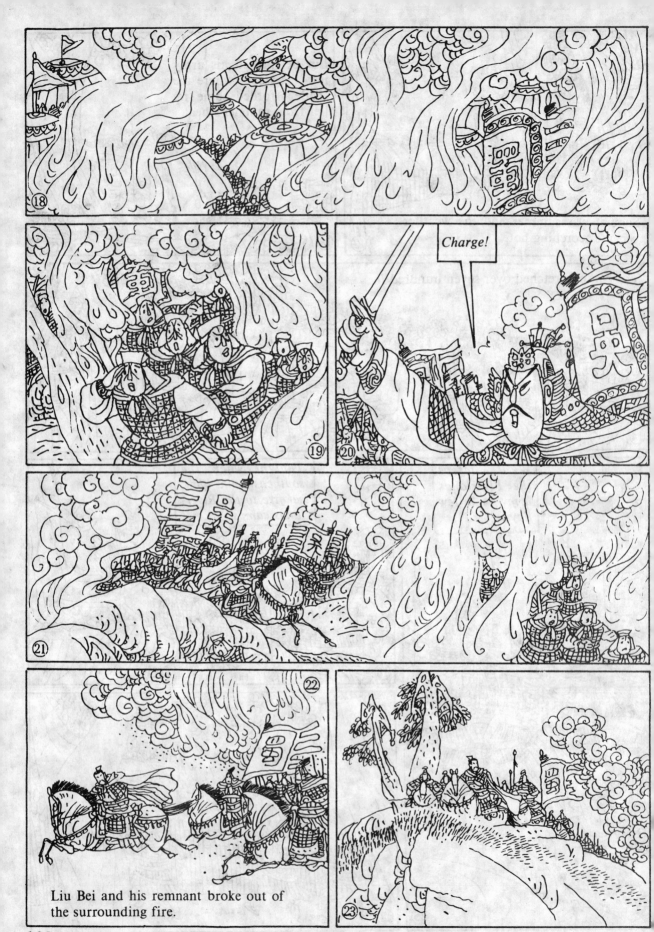

Liu Bei and his remnant broke out of the surrounding fire.

Liu Bei was very distressed.

Here the Southland army comes!

Set fire in the valley to block them.

Liu Bei fled to Baidi in panic.

139

Liu Bei was caught by a disease.

Liu Bei sent for Zhuge Liang.

Liu Bei trusted state affairs to Zhuge Liang.

Liu Bei died at Baidi.

The crown prince Liu Shan became the emperor of Shu.

The Tianshui Pass

Zhuge Liang attacked Nan'an and captured the chief commander of the Wei army, Xiahou Mao.

①

Zhuge Liang had a man impersonate Pei Xu and then sent him to Tianshui.

②

The false Pei Xu went to see Ma Zun, the governor of Tianshui.

③

I'm here to seek the assistance of Tianshui and Anding districts for the emergency in Nan'an.

④

I'll send my troops to relieve Nan'an immediately.

This man is a Riverlands commander in disguise whose intention is to trick you into leaving Tianshui so that they can take it.

General. Jiang Wei recognized it as Zhuge Liang's trap.

Jiang Wei offered Ma Zun a plan which Ma Zun adopted with pleasure.

According to Jiang Wei's plan, Ma Zun led his troops out of the city.

Zhao Yun with a company of troops came to attack Tianshui.

Jiang Wei and his force sprang out and surrounded them.

⑪

Zhao Yun, Jiang Wei of Hanshui! Here before you!

⑫

⑬

Zhao Yun was surprised that such a general existed in Tianshui.

⑭

⑮

Ma Zun and his men returned.

⑯

Zhao Yun had no way but to go back.

When I decided to take Tianshui, I never expected to find such a man! Let me have him submit.

Zhuge Liang sent Wei Yan to pretend that he was going to capture Yicheng.

Zhao Yun took the order to attack Shanggui.

Jiang Wei appealed to Ma Zun to go to rescue Yicheng, where his mother lived.

Jiang Wei advanced toward Yicheng with his troops.

Wei Yan feigned defeat and fled.

Jiang Wei entered Yicheng.

I am Jiang Wei. I've already surrendered to Shu. Quickly offer your city and submit.

Zhuge Liang had someone impersonate Jiang Wei, challenging the city of Tianshui.

Zhuge Liang led his troops in an attack on Yicheng.

The grain in the city is too scare. Let me seize Zhuge Liang's supplies.

The hidden Riverlands army sprang out.

Jiang Wei tried to re-enter Yicheng, but found the flags of Shu flying on the walls.

Jiang Wei forced a way through without any followers.

Jiang Wei headed for Tianshui alone.

Jiang Wei has submitted to Shu. Shoot him.

41

42 *Yin Shang and Liang Xu are agents collaborating with Jiang Wei. I must have them killed first.*

43 *Ma Zun wants to kill us. Better for us to deliver the city to the Riverlands and surrender.*

44 Liang Xu and Yin Shang threw the city gate open and invited the Shu army to come in.

45 Zhuge Liang and his troops entered.

Sima Yi Captures Meng Da

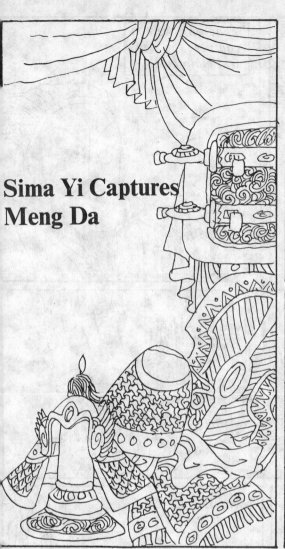

The ruler of Wei, Cao Rui, met successive defeats and could find no way out.

①

We can summon Sima Yi back to handle this.

Do you know a man who is capable of repelling the Riverlands army?

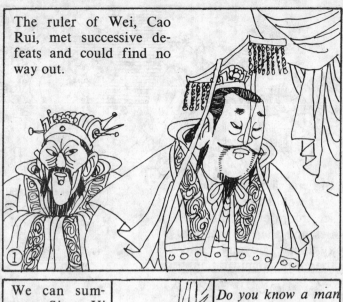

②

Cao Rui called in Sima Yi.

③

Cao Rui restored Sima Yi's former office, and adding the title Field Marshal Who Conquers the West. He ordered Sima Yi to confront the Riverlands army.

④

149

Li Feng said: Meng Da of Wei would like to mobilize troops of the three cities and then take action against Luoyang, and therefore submit to Shu.

That way, we can capture the central plain easily.

Sima Yi raised his troops to confront Shu.

Meng Da is ambitious, but he's no match for Sima Yi; he will only be captured.

Meng Da had Zhuge Liang's letter.

Quickly go to forewarn Meng Da.

150

Meng Da asked the messenger to tell Zhuge Liang not to worry.

Someone told Sima Yi about Meng Da's defection.

Sima Yi decided to remove Meng Da first.

Set out for Xincheng and destroy the defector Meng Da.

Sima Yi and his troops marched to Xincheng at top speed.

Meng Da, governor of Jincheng Shen Yi and governor of Shangyong Shen Dan, were in discussion about the action.

We don't have enough equipment and provisions.

Before Sima Yi arrives, tomorrow we'll raise the banner of Han and collect all our forces to directly attack Luoyang.

Xu Huang, vanguard of Sima Yi's troops, arrived, challenging outside the city.

Traitor Meng Da! Surrender now!

Xu Huang was shot through the forehead.

The army of Sima Yi came from all directions.

Meng Da sealed the gates and refused to fight.

A warrior reported: The armies of Shen Dan and Shen Yi have arrived.

They come for our rescue. Open the gates and go out to fight.

Traitor Meng Da! Halt! Here is Shen Dan!

Meng Da realized he had been deceived and rode back toward the city.

Meng Da, we have delivered the city.

Meng Da turned back and fled, Shen Dan was in pursuit.

Ah!

The Empty-City Trick

Sima Yi marched west through the passes to defeat the army of Shu.

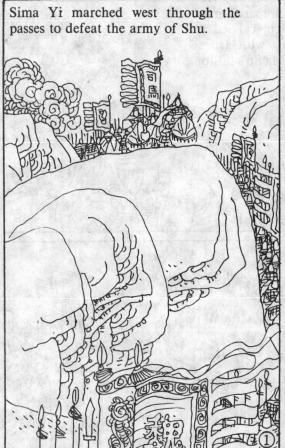

Sima Yi will try to take Jieting and cut off our main route.

Military Adviser Ma Su volunteered to defend Jieting.

However insignificant Jieting may seem, it is vital to the survival of our main army. Sima Yi is no ordinary general, I don't think you are a match for him.

You'll have my oath: you have my life if anything goes wrong.

Zhuge Liang dispatched the leading commander Wang Ping to go with Ma Su.

Ignoring Wang Ping's warning, Ma Su pitched camp on the hill.

Wang Ping had to pitch a small camp at the foot of the hill.

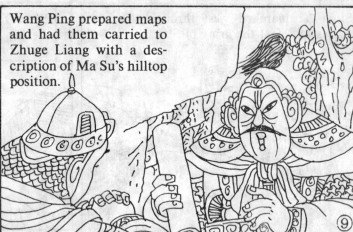

Wang Ping prepared maps and had them carried to Zhuge Liang with a description of Ma Su's hilltop position.

Sima Yi arrived at Jieting.

The Riverlands army has pitched their camp on the hill. Jieting looks easy to capture.

Cut off the water conduits and set fire to the hill.

The soldiers could not stand being thirsty.

Ma Su ordered his men to go down but they had lost their heart and refused to do it.

Wang Ping intended to come to the rescue but his army was hopelessly out-numbered, so he had to withdraw.

Ma Su forced his way down the hill and fled.

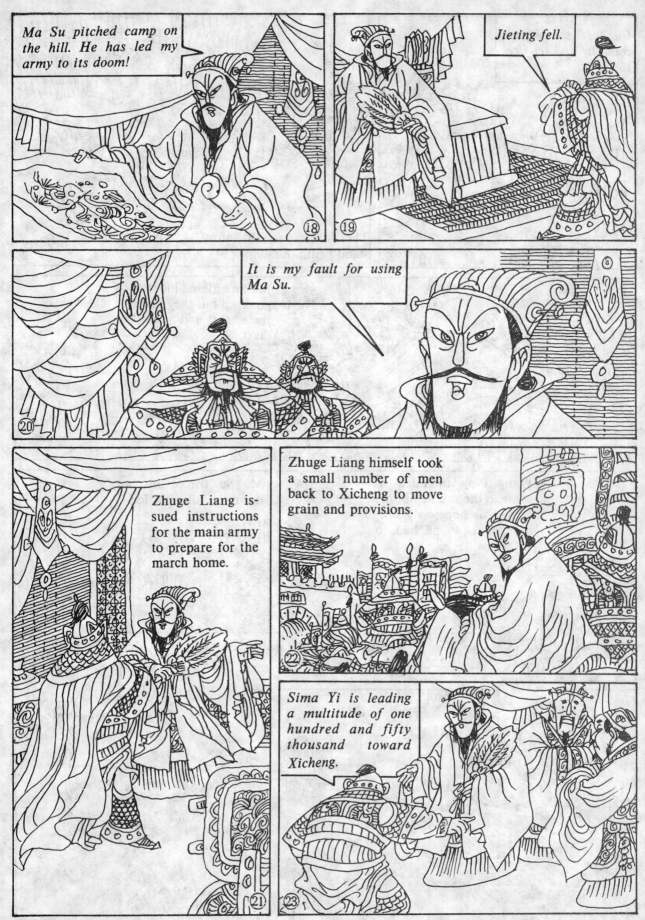

We have no commanders, only a group of civil officials and a small number of soldiers. What shall we do?

Put out of sight all flags and banners, leave four gates opened wide and have some soldiers disguised as commoners and let them sweep the roadway.

Zhuge Liang is sitting on the wall by the turret, burning incense as he plays. And the music sounds nothing different. How strange!

Zhuge Liang has always been a man of extreme caution, never one to tempt Fate. He opened the gates because he has set up an ambush. Withdraw.

Could Zhuge Liang be staging this because he has no troops?

Though Sima Yi has withdrawn, he is sure to come back. Quickly ask the people of Xicheng to follow the troops into Hanzhong.

We see Shu banners in the midst of dust before us.

Zhuge Liang really has an ambush here. Let's go!

The Riverlands army has retreated to Hanzhong.

I was deceived by Zhuge Liang's "Empty-City Trick."

Ma Su lost Jieting and bungled the chance of winning the battle. Have him removed and executed.

Zhuge Liang had the troops put through rigorous training, stockpiled grain and provisions, preparing for battle against the north again.

Zhuge Liang wrote a petition and presented it to the court requesting his own demotion from the position of prime minister.

The Formation of Eight Trigrams

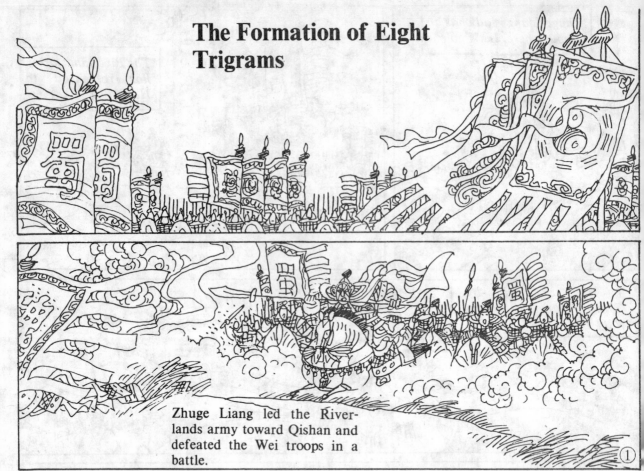

Zhuge Liang led the River-lands army toward Qishan and defeated the Wei troops in a battle. ①

Cao Zhen was in such a bad mood that he fell ill in bed.

②

Zhuge Liang let captured Wei soldiers take back a letter, which humiliated Cao Zhen.

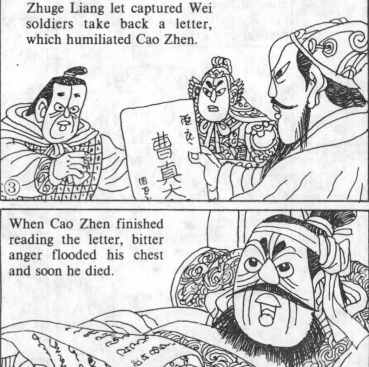
③

When Cao Zhen finished reading the letter, bitter anger flooded his chest and soon he died. ④

Sima Yi sent Zhuge Liang a call to battle.

⑤

Zhuge Liang accepted the challenge.

⑥

⑦

Zhuge Liang, let two of us decide here and now which is the rooster and which the hen!

⑧

Do you want to fight with commanders? With troops? Or with orders of battle?

⑨

First with orders of battle!

⑩

Can you name this array?

Our lowest commander could do that one—the "Beginning of Form."

Sima Yi, do you recognize it?

The Formation of Eight Trigrams!

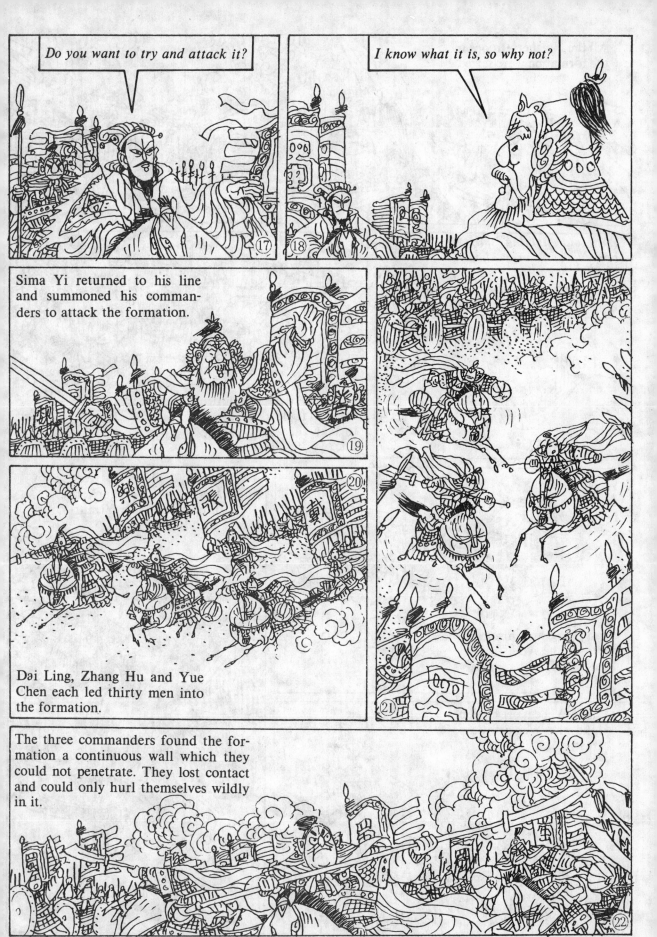

All the Northern troops in the formation were seized.

With our fighting spirit broken, how can we hold up our heads before the high officials of the North?

Sima Yi ordered his entire army to fight to the death to take the enemy battle line.

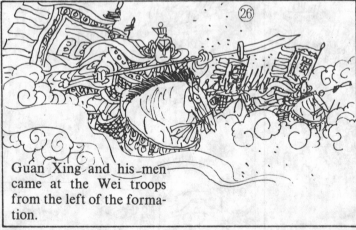

Guan Xing and his men came at the Wei troops from the left of the formation.

Riverlands soldiers were squeezing the Northerners from three sides. Sima Yi hurriedly withdrew.

Jiang Wei cut off from behind the Wei army's retreat.

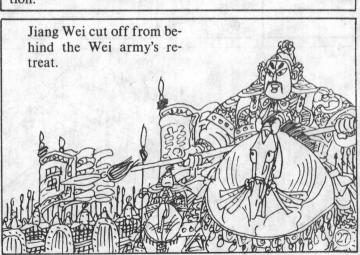

Sima Yi guided the entire Wei force to fight desperately to break out of the formation.

Give my order to reward the army.

Burning with resentment, Gou An fled to the Wei camp.

District Commander Gou An was responsible for delivering a shipment of grain to Zhuge Liang; it arrived ten days past the deadline. Zhuge Liang ordered guards to give him eighty strokes with a staff.

Go back to Chengdu and spread rumors. Better get your ruler to recall Zhuge Liang.

Gou An spread rumors in Chengdu.

Zhuge Liang's pride in his achievements would soon lead him to usurp the ruling house.

Summon Zhuge Liang back to court.

I am about to accomplish something important. If I go back, another chance like this will be hard to come by.

Zhuge Liang ordered his troops to withdraw.

Wuzhangyuan

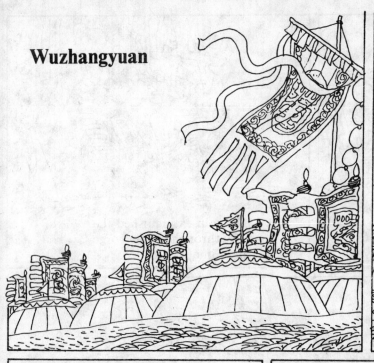

Zhuge Liang led his troops toward the Qishan Hills for the sixth time and staged an ambush at Shangfang Gorge.

①

When Sima Yi's troops entered the gorge, the ambushing troops rose out and cut off their road back.

②

The Riverlands army set fire in the gorge; this blocked the entrance to the gorge.

③

We are doomed to die here.

④

169

Suddenly a stormy wind raced down the valley, in the wake of that torrents of rain gushed down.

⑤

⑥

The rain extinguished the fires throughout the gorge and Sima Yi escaped.

Sima Yi and his remnant retreated to his Weibei camp.

⑦

Zhuge Liang stationed himself at Wuzhangyuan.

⑧

Sima Yi refused battle.

⑨

Zhuge Liang sent Sima Yi a maiden's dress and a letter to humiliate him.

⑩

So he takes me for a woman.

How is Zhuge Liang?

The prime minister rises early and works late. He personally sees to many trifles and he doesn't eat very much.

Zhuge Liang got anxious when Sima Yi refused to fight.

Zhuge Liang can't last too long.

Fei Yi reported that the Wei army had defeated the Wu army in Hefei and their morale was rising.

I am near the end.

Quickly call Jiang Wei to see me.

Zhuge Liang transmitted to Jiang Wei the twenty-four military essays which he had written.

Ma Dai, after I am dead, Wei Yan will turn against us. Carry out my plan after my death.

Yang Yi, after I am dead, Wei Yan will turn against us. Carry out my plan and you will find the right man to execute him.

Zhuge Liang fell into unconsciousness until night.

Come with me to inspect the camps.

Never shall I go to the front and fight the rebels again!

Yang Yi, after my death, make a slow and deliberate retreat. Jiang Wei has the wit and courage to protect the rear.

Should Sima Yi pursue, set the wooden statue I've carved in my wagon and push it to the front.

Zhuge Liang passed away.

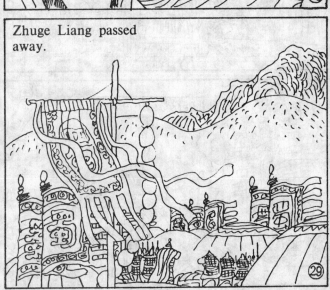

The Riverlands army made a slow retreat.

A Wei general reported: The River-lands army has evacuated!

So Zhuge Liang has died. Pursue them at once!

The Riverlands troops are not far ahead.

Suddenly a bombard sounded and the Riverlands army turned back to face Sima Yi.

Zhuge Liang is alive. We are trapped again. Withdraw!

Retreat at once!

174

On the Wei army's retreat, Jiang Wei ordered his men to approach the plank road.

Wei Yan really turned against us!

Wei Yan had burned the wooden plank road and deployed troops to bar the route.

Take the small road around the wooden plank road.

175

His Excellency never did you ill! How dare you turn against him now?

I dare you to shout three times the words "Who dares slay me?"

Who dares slay me!....

Ma Dai came up and cut Wei Yan down from his horse.

Go back to Chengdu to report to the Second Emperor.

The Second Emperor Liu Shan demanded to bury Zhuge Liang on Dingjun Mountain.

Battle of Wits Between Jiang Wei and Deng Ai

Jiang Wei petitioned the court to give him the order to attack Wei.

Jiang Wei moved his army towards Qishan Hills.

He pitched his camps at Qishan Hills.

Jiang Wei ordered Bao Su to position his forces at the entrance of the hills, and he himself led strong troops to attack Nan'an.

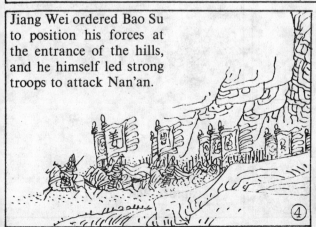

Wei general Deng Ai was inspecting the situation of the Riverlands army.

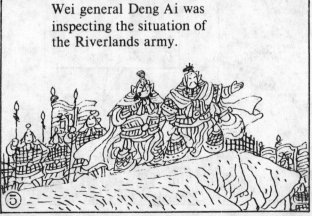

General Chen Tai, Jiang Wei is bound to go to attack Nan'an. You can follow my plan,....

⑥

⑦

Deng Ai guided his troops to rescue Nan'an.

Chen Tai crushed the Riverlands army at the entrance of the Qishan Hills and killed Bao Su.

⑧

Jiang Wei and his troops was approaching Nan'an.

⑨

I have fallen into Deng Ai's trap.

⑩

⑪

Jiang Wei turned back to Shanggui, intending to capture Wei's grain.

Jiang Wei led his troops to Duan Valley.

Behind the hill much dust is rising. There must be an ambush there.

Retreat quickly.

Deng Ai's son Deng Zhong attacked from the left.

Wei general Shi Zuan came at Jiang Wei's army from the right.

Deng Ai attacked from the third direction.

The Riverlands army was surrounded.

The Riverlands general Zhang Yi came to rescue Jiang Wei, and he himself was killed by Wei arrows.

Jiang Wei broke through the encirclement and retreated to Hanzhong.

Jiang Wei guided the Riverlands troops towards the Qishan Hills again.

Jiang Wei pitched his camp at the entrance to the gorge.

I've had a tunnel dug under the ground reaching the Riverlands camp. Go through the tunnel to attack the left camp of the enemy tonight at the third watch.

Deng Zhong and Shi Zuan attacked from the left and right.

At midnight, Zheng Lun's army emerged from underground.

Deng Zhong and Shi Zuan, strike the Riverlands camps respectively from the left and right.

Shoot them down with bows.

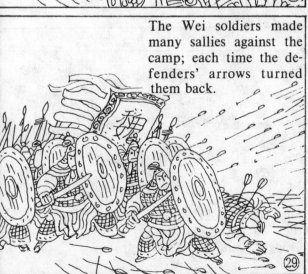

The Wei soldiers made many sallies against the camp; each time the defenders' arrows turned them back.

The next day Jiang Wei placed the Formation of Eight Trigrams.

Deng Ai also placed the same order.

Deng Ai, do you think you can circumvent my order?

Why not?

Jiang Wei waved his spear and the formation changed to "Serpent Coiled on the Ground."

What is this formation called?

Deng Ai was surrounded.

Sima Wang broke through the encirclement and brought Deng Ai to safety.

Deng Ai retreated to the south bank of the Wei River and camped there.

All nine camps of Qishan were captured by the Riverlands army.

Deng Ai asked Sima Wang to pin down Jiang Wei. He himself would leave to retake the Qishan camps.

Deng Ai got just behind the hills when Liao Hua and his men emerged in ambush.

Liao Hua killed the Wei general Zheng Lun.

Deng Ai broke through the encirclement.

Deng Ai planned to use the stratagem of sowing distrust to force Jiang Wei to retreat.

Deng Ai sent people to Chengdu to spread rumors, which would cause Liu Shan to call Jiang Wei back.

The eunuch Huang Hao framed Jiang Wei before the emperor, saying that Jiang Wei was about to submit to Wei.

Order Jiang Wei to withdraw immediately.

Jiang Wei led his troops back.

184

Three Kingdoms Became United as the Jin Dynasty

① Deng Ai raised the Wei army to attack Shu in A.D. 263.

② *Deng Ai has reached the city gates of Chengdu. What shall I do?*

③ Liu Shan, with his hands tied behind him, opened the gate and submitted. The kingdom of Shu was destroyed.

④ Jiang Wei feigned surrender to Wei general Zhong Hui, intending to seek chances to restore the sovereignty of Shu.

⑤ Jiang Wei offered a plan to Zhong Hui, suggesting he kill Deng Ai.

185

Zhong Hui arrested Deng Ai and his son for planning a revolt.

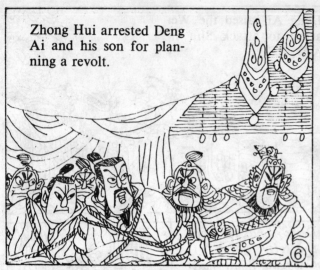

Wei general Wei Huan killed Deng Ai and his son when escorting them to Luoyang.

Jiang Wei talked Zhong Hui into a revolt against Wei, planning, in the confusion, to bring Liu Shan to resume Shu.

The secret was found out and Zhong Hui was killed by arrows. Jiang Wei killed himself with his sword.

After Sima Zhao died of illness, Sima Yan became the king of Jin.

Sima Yan deposed the emperor of Wei and established the Jin Dynasty.

The emperor of Wu, Sun Hao, wanted to raise his troops to attack Jin.

Now that the Kingdom of Shu has been overthrown, Sima Yan will aim to swallow Wu. It would behoove Your Majesty to develop your virtue and bring security to the people of the Southland. It's not the right time for a war.

How dare you oppose me. Remove and execute him.

Those who dare to disobey my wish again will be beheaded.

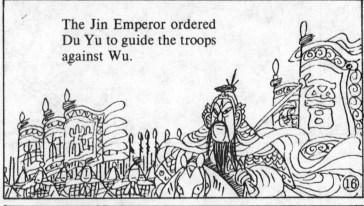

The Jin Emperor ordered Du Yu to guide the troops against Wu.

Du Yu led land and marine forces towards Jianye, capital of Wu.

Jin's marine force went along the Great River, approaching Wu.

(19) Du Yu led the land force directly to Jianye.

(20) All Wu troops they met on their way surrendered.

(21) Jin's marine force neared Wu's boundary.

(22)

(23) *There are iron stakes embedded under the water, the bottoms of our ships have been torn.*

(24) Wang Jun had the stakes pulled out of the riverbed.

Wang Jun asked his men to place large torches on the rafts, which melted the iron and the chains across the river separated.

Pound the war drums and march to Jianye.

The Jin army reached the city gates of Jianye.

189

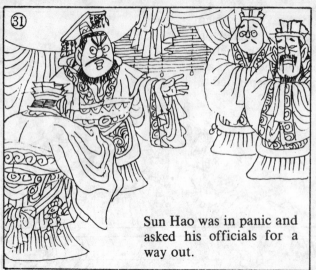

Sun Hao was in panic and asked his officials for a way out.

Someone suggested that Sun Hao follow the model set by Liu Shan.

Admitting his failure, Sun Hao, with his hands tied behind him, had the gates opened.

The Kingdom of Wu was destroyed.

Thereafter, the three kingdoms came under the rule of the Jin Emperor. An era of separated kingdoms was concluded.